Tales
and
Legends
of
Morocco

Tales and Legends of Morocco

ELISA CHIMENTI

TRANSLATED BY ARNON BENAMY

AN ASTOR BOOK

IVAN OBOLENSKY, INC.
New York

Contents

Introduction   xi
Prologue   1
The Legend of the Almond Tree   5
Oum-Hani   6
The Origin of Tangier   10
The First Diamond   12
Satan's Mirror   15
Bou-Louan   21
The Legend of El-Minar   27
The Meteorite of Torre Blanquilla   31
The Butterflies   32
The Lizard   34
The Legend of the Stars   35
The Sage of Tanger el-Balia   37
The Algerian Bracelets   41
The Cadi and the Jewish Merchant   53
The Three Curses of Sidi Abderrahman of Mejdoub   57
The Legend of Gold   60
The Pearls   62
Why the Bee Dies When It Stings a Human Being   63
The Legend of the Monkeys   64
The Cedar Tree of Sidi Bou-Mehada   66

The Owl   67

Tobacco   71

The Olive Tree   72

The Donkey of Moulay Bou-Azza   74

The Prophet and the Gazelle   76

The Embroidered *Bedaiah*   78

The Legend of Sidi Ali ben Hamdouch   105

The Origin of Prayer Beads   106

The Sun and the Moon   107

Ibliss and the Peasant   108

Be Resigned to Your Fate If You Would
     Please Allah   113

Mother, Mother . . .   115

Quinza the Hairdresser   117

The Birds of the Prophet   119

The Water-Carrier   120

The Fig Tree   123

Zeineb   125

Why Man Must Struggle to Obtain His Daily Bread   127

The Almond Tree   129

Fekroune the Tortoise   131

The Chameleon   132

Abdullah the Highwayman   134

The Dream of the Sage's Wife   140

Why the Mohammedan Does Not Eat Pork   144

How Sidna Youssef Invented the Clock   145

The Dogs of Tangier   148

The Crow   149

Glossary   151

Tales
and
Legends
of
Morocco

Introduction

The folklore of Morocco is a harmonious synthesis of its ideas, its history of wars, invasions and conquests, and its beliefs—all that the human imagination can produce that is both terrifying and beautiful.

Much of the material in this book was collected in Tangier, and it should be noted that the tales and legends of this ancient city differ from those of other regions of Morocco in that they are neither purely Arabic nor purely Berber. The masculine spirit of the Arab and the rustic spirit of the Berber halt at the edge of essentially feminine Tangier.

The origin of Tangier harks back to remote antiquity. Its existence is acknowledged in the myths of Hercules and Atlas. One legend would have it that it was founded by Melkarth, the Phoenician counterpart of Hercules, who separated Europe from Africa by the great strength of his arm. A Moroccan tale assures us that it was founded by Noah at the beginning of the earth's existence. On the other hand, the Greeks insist that it was founded by Antaeus (son of Neptune) during the Heroic Age. It was established on the day the angels fell in love with the daughters of man, says another ancient fable.

If we are to believe Vergil in his fourth book of *The Aeneid,* a god was the first visitor to Morocco, or perhaps it was Og, the giant king of Basara, who survived the

Deluge by clinging to Noah's Ark. The Argonauts, fleeing the wrath of Aeëtes, hid in the port of Tangier. Aboul-Zeid of the Beni-Hillal clan came here as a conquerer as did Seif Ettijani, the mighty swordsman who waged war against magicians and the jinn (genies).

Thus Tangier became the cradle of strange myths and legends in which fable and history formed threads with which poets of imagination wove a brilliant tapestry.

So much for the legend. Now let us examine the facts of history. From the shadows of pre-history only undecipherable symbols remain; long-forgotten languages were found engraved on coins and funeral plaques. Strabo (Greek geographer, 63 B.C.) would have us believe they were of Hindu origin. Sallust (Roman historian, 86 B.C.) thought they might be Persian or Armenian. Procopius (Byzantine historian, A.D. 527) was of the opinion they might have belonged to Canaanites vanquished and driven out by Joshua or to wandering tribes separated from the historic family tree of Noah.

Scholars who base their knowledge on cuneiform inscriptions say that certain princes named Gomar, Elischa and Tarnaschich were the first to reach the shores of Morocco.

The Phoenicians, who settled in Tangier more than a thousand years before Christ, made of it a highly important city with splendid palaces and sumptuous temples that were dominated from the heights by the sanctuary of Baal, god of the city; this is confirmed by coins found at Tamoudda and elsewhere representing Baal carrying a sovereign's scepter. Moroccan legend (which is history in poetic form) assures us that the most ancient ruins of Tangier belonged to a race of sun-worshipers, the Chemich.

The Phoenicians brought with them pottery, weapons, fabrics, guns and magic resins, the relics of the ancient religions of Chaldea and the popular religious myths of Mesopotamia, which are peopled with the gods, jinn, giants and monsters (which can be found in many of our legends), as well as the tales of their struggles against Sargon, Nebuchadnezzar and Alexander the Great.

Roman conquerors transformed Tangier into the metropolis of Mauretania. They brought their civilization, their eternal monuments, and the smiling divinities of Latin mythology (who replaced the somber, cruel gods of Tyre and Carthage).

The Hebrews who established themselves in Cyrenaica long before the reign of Augustus visited our land three centuries before Christ and made many converts among the inhabitants, paving the way for monotheistic Islam.

Christianity came late to Mauretania. The North Africans were among the last to accept the new faith, according to the historian Petilianus. Remnants of Christian belief still remain among certain Mohammedan tribes in the interior of Morocco. They observe Sunday by doing no weaving on that day, and they regard the cross as a powerful magic symbol.

Tangier, just as Rome and Alexandria, was the scene of thousand-year-old beliefs and revelations which fought to obtain supremacy over men's souls. Together with the psalms of King David and the sublime song of Job rose the sound of citterns accompanying hymns to pale Astarte (Phoenician goddess).

The Arabs who had brought Islam to North Africa turned Tangier into a *nezala* ("rest-camp") for the Mohammedan soldiers who were carrying on an invasion of Spain from Moroccan shores. We know that in the late fifteenth century they were expelled from Spain by Ferdinand and Isabella, together with the Jews who had accompanied them earlier to that land. These Sephardic Jews returned to Tangier charged like bees with the honey of Hebrew legends and the tales of Castile and León—touching ballads which were sung to crades in the *mellah* ("ghetto").

The Spaniards, the Portuguese and the English built walls around the city, only to abandon them later on. These and other invasions brought to Tangier an inexhaustible treasury of traditions and legends—the somber tales of the Phoenicians, the poetic myths of the Greeks, the heroic epics of the Romans, the Islamic creed from Arabia and Persia— all amalgamated into a thousand strange and charming tales wherein men are transformed into giants, heroes into gods, and kings into jinn. Thus the Numido-Mauretanian kings Masinissa, Bocchus, Bogud and Ptolemy were fused into a single glorious defender of Islam, conqueror of giants and infidels. Thus, Baal, the sun-god, no longer cast his rays at the base of temples, for he had become Chem-Harouch, and like Pluto he reigned in the depths of the earth.

A Tangier poet once said, "Our folklore is the brilliant dust of civilizations that have since disappeared. These masterpieces of successive generations are purely Moroccan and obey the forms of our art. They resemble the clear sky of the West, the earth that is rich with flowers, our palaces with their sober purity of line, the harmonious proportions of a young woman and the proud virility of a Mohammedan warrior." In these primitive fables of the market place, ancient divinities, jinn, horrendous—or more often gentle— supernatural beings haunt grottoes, forests and springs. Sidi Masmoun, in other times known as Saturn, abandons his subterranean kingdom and hides in the cannons of the old fortresses. During the perfume-scented nights, jinniyeh (female genies) steal into the Moorish quarters to kiss the lips of sleeping youths. When the full-moon is reflected

xiv

with silver clarity on the leaves of the olive groves of Cherf el-Aquab, Tingisé the fairy, followed by her companion, Chem-Harouch, seek the purple flower which alone brings happiness.

Although it is difficult to separate the diverse elements of which the *Tales and Legends* are composed, one is nevertheless aware of five definite sources. Our first group is composed of legends that date from the furthest antiquity and recall the Hindu, Semitic and Greco-Roman polytheism that existed prior to Islam. Such for instance is "The Meteorite of Torre Blanquilla," the legend of the *faquih* (teacher of the Koran) of Torre Blanquilla, another Icarius, who borrows wings from the jinn in order to gather a bouquet of stars in the sky. Here is the reflection of mythologies in which countries and centuries mingle freely and superstitions reach back to the first stages of the world.

The second group of Moroccan legends are those of Islamic origin and are by far the most numerous. Some are rich in pastoral paintings, with comparisons and examples taken from the lives of *fellahin* ("peasants") and nomads; they have the tranquil aspect of our plains and are as simple in experience as they are rich in dreams. There are accounts of bravery and faith, of exploits of the warriors of the Crescent, of the grandeur of sultans who held sway over Morocco at different periods in her history. There are religious, naive stories of saints, healers and miracles, such as "The First Diamond"; the story of El-Minar, whose tower dominates the Strait of Gibraltar to this day; "Satan's Mirror"; "The Birds of the Prophet"; "Quinza the Hairdresser"; "The Legend of The Almond Tree," and a great many others. Each of these tales pulsates with the joy of generosity, a love of mankind, and with faith and respect for the Creator as well as submission to His will.

The third group of legends and tales which are part of

Morocco's heritage come from the Sephardic (Spanish-Jewish) community. These Spanish Jews produced an inexhaustible richness of tales and wisdom. These are stories of patriarchs and prophets of Israel, of kings and noblemen of medieval Spain and of an earlier Morocco. Uniting an Asiatic and Spanish base into a Moroccan form, they have the somber grandeur and the nobility of passages from the Bible. In this group may be placed "The Cadi and the Jewish Merchant."

The fourth group of stories are those which were strongly influenced by Christianity, which came before, but continued during, the reign of Islam in Morocco. Our Lord Jesus Christ (who had never been in Northwest Africa despite what the story-tellers may say in the market place) was supposed to have visited our *douars* (Arab tent villages) and our *ighrems* (fortified Berber towns). Here he offered charity, revived the dead and performed miracles. Like the women of Morocco who at winter's end go into the orange groves to greet the arrival of spring, the Virgin Mary was reputed to have visited the orchards of Souani and the rose-perfumed gardens of Jebel Kbir.

Martyrs and saints came in a direct line from the "Golden Legend," and like the gods of the Homeric sagas they intervene in the affairs of men, punish the jinn and the evil forces which menace the children of Adam, and combat the mysterious forces which turn away true Believers from the road to salvation.

These touching and at times tragic tales condense the spirit of a Christianity that was more fanatic than pious, tempered by the great wisdom of the Arabs and by their profound sense of destiny and resignation. Of the sacred fire lit in Africa by the zeal of Saint Cyprian and Saint Augustine there remain such stories as "Zeineb," in which a peasant's wife is raised from the dead by the Prophet Jesus; "Abdullah the Highwayman"; and the story of Lass el-

xvi

Behar, the blond pirate with light-green eyes who might have come out of a Nordic saga.

The fifth group of legends is like a fine black thread running through the multicolored pattern of Moroccan folklore; they have their source in Bled el-Abid, the "land of the slaves." Naive, extremely childlike, these fables have their roots in the beliefs of very primitive Africans of the interior. Their stories deal most often with magic plants, sacred animals and sacred precious stones. Under Islamic influence their jinn have been deprived of their former glory. Respected only because they are feared, they lurk in the dark depth of pools and moan lugubriously in the night whenever one of the Faithful is about to depart this world. Incense is burned in honor of these spirits by superstitious women and by Negroes during their *Derdebat* (religious séance). "The Pearls," the story of a jinniyeh who loves a mortal, may be entered in this category.

And so princes, warriors, sultans, heroes and wise men rise from the historic past through the rustic voice of a story-teller as he dazzles his simple listeners in the market place. In time this folklore, like a delicate flower, is doomed to fade with the advent of modern civilization. Soon few will remember the princesses and jinn who enthralled humanity at its infancy. Lalla Hania ("Tranquillity"), who had brought peace to our homes, has gone and with her has also gone Lalla Mekouna, our "Protectress." Naiads no longer spread their golden tresses on the surface of ponds and spirits with forked feet have ceased to dance in the heart of the cedar forests. The magic syllables whose sweetness and power evoked the jinn no longer pass the lips of skeptical scholars. In the Moorish cafés the song of the *guenbri* (Berber lute) vibrates with the sadness of a poignant adieu.

ELISA CHIMENTI
Tangiers, 1932

Prologue

We are in the native market place which lies within the casbah of a Moroccan town. Blind Mahjoub, the storyteller, is in the center of a circle of spellbound listeners who are eagerly drinking in his tales of caliphs, jinn (genies) and saints, of enchanted gardens and alabaster palaces.

"In the name of Allah!" he cries and gently strikes the tambourine in his hand, for it is with these words that he begins a new story.

"Allah is mighty," the crowd murmurs in response.

"In the name of Allah and may prayer and salvation be upon His prophet!" continues Mahjoub. "Praise to Allah whose attributes are too numerous to count, for He is the omnipotent Master of the Universe. May Allah spread His benedictions on our Lord Mohammed, the Torch in the Darkness, the Guide of the Just . . . Amen!"

"Amen," reply the onlookers.

The ancient storyteller pauses a moment, he raises his sightless eyes toward the sky, murmurs a prayer and begins his tale.

"And it so happened, O creatures of Allah, that there was once a sultan whose palace was guarded by jinn . . ."

The audience—mountaineers, peasants and artisans—come closer to Mahjoub; in a frail and slow voice he repeats a

1

legend gathered from the lips of a Berber storyteller, a story born under a nomad's tent while his flock slept within the enclosure of a temporary village. Or perhaps it is a tale which survived from ancient Assyria, from Egypt or from Persia—a tale ringing with the clash of arms, peopled with the jinn, sparkling with precious stones and scented with sandalwood and roses.

"Ajouba! Greatest of wonders!" cries the crowd.

Sous and pieces of silver begin to rain into a wooden bowl that stands on the ground near Mahjoub. Some of the peasants move away; others take their places and edge in closer. A poem follows in honor of Saint Moulay Idriss, founder of the city of Fez; then there is a long saga of oriental chivalry—love, generosity and vengeance among the nomadic tribes. Stories follow upon stories in a seemingly endless succession; there is Abderrahman, who cursed the town of Alcazar and threatened the inhabitants with blindness; Mawyia, daughter of Tarafa, who was urged by Ibliss (Allah curse the demon) to abandon her husband; El-Mehdi, a learned scholar of the Koran, who borrowed the wings of a jinni in order to gather a bouquet of stars for a sultan's daughter; Antar, as formidable in death as in life; Aboul-Zeid, son of Hadra, the warrior who was black as the wings of a crow; Seif Ettijani, the scourge of kings, who fought magicians and jinn. Dervishes, sultans, warriors and saints pray, love, fight and die in this enchanted world.

It is late afternoon. Wasps buzz around the overripe fruit in the market place; flies tangle their feet and wings in honey made sticky by the hot sun. The water-carriers have ceased ringing their bells. Overcome by the heat, beggars and stray dogs lie sleeping in the shadow of the walls. The minarets reflect the sunlight in great flashes of fire. There is an odor of moist skin, of incense and of hashish in the air.

2

The voice of the storyteller becomes more grave, more remote. He leaves the domain of the purely fanciful and turns to history.

"The Prophet, prayer and salvation be upon him, lived many centuries ago in Arabia. In order to spread his teachings, Mohammedan warriors went forth to conquer the world; a hundred powerful nations fell before the unvanquished Crescent."

Mahjoub's voice is full of triumph. "A thousand Oriental palaces rose in Christian lands. In Cordova, beloved city of the caliphs, the three thousand minarets of its three thousand mosques pointed toward the heavens. The Alhambra was set like a jewel in the gold hills of Granada."

"Glory to Allah!" cries the crowd with one voice.

"All that is perfect soon becomes imperfect," continues the storyteller. "Defeat follows victory. Our ancestors abandoned the palaces of Andalusia; they took refuge in Morocco where a glorious descendant of the Prophet, prayer and salvation be upon him, welcomed them with open arms. But alas, he could not make them forget Granada and Andalusia, for no magic or sorcery can efface from the heart of the refugee a longing for the country he has left behind. Time passed. The Occident armed; infidels invaded the lands of Islam. Where were the invincible princes of the past? They had exchanged their glorious palaces for the darkness of the tomb; gone, too, were their warriors. The Believers fell under the swords of the Christians. Glory to Allah, for thus has it been written . . ."

But suddenly there is a change in Mahjoub's voice; it becomes vibrant and joyous. Now he speaks of the glorious future of the Faithful, of the day when they will have cast off their sins and will march in the path of Allah.

"Because of your sins, O Mohammedans, the sky of your glory is clouded, but he who repents is pardoned."

Mahjoub is no longer a feeble old man with a trembling

hand extended to the passers-by. He is a poet, a magician who creates a whole world of beauty and light, a prophet of Biblical times speaking to the people in the name of Jehovah.

The sunset approaches with its tones of amber and gold. A fresh breeze comes out of the west; the leaves of the palm trees rustle gently. From a minaret comes the strident call of a muezzin; the storyteller grows still before this vibrant voice which declaims the grandeur of Allah. Heads bow, lips murmur in prayer. Mahjoub's humble audience gradually disperses, carrying away the promise of a dream, the hope of future grandeur, if it please Allah.

O storytellers of the market place, wandering poets of Islam, consolers of the poor and the afflicted, dispensers of magic words, inspired singers of noble traditions and ancient virtues—be with us until that day when humanity will have no further need of dreams.

The Legend of the Almond Tree

Those who do good deeds will receive the benediction of the Lord and He will show them mercy.—The Koran

Before the advent of Islam, there was a beautiful and generous young princess in the land of Sous. Her name was Hatim and she was of the tribe of Tai. Much of the wealth she distributed to the poor was her own, but she also gave money belonging to her father, the sultan.

"Allah will forgive me for taking the wealth of others," she said to herself, "for He will see to what good purpose it is used."

The sultan was informed of his daughter's "generosity"; she was brought before him and he admonished her severely.

"Your wealth belongs to you and you are free to dispose of it in any way that you wish," he said, "but what right do you have to distribute money which belongs to me?"

"Can I refuse to help the aged and the unfortunate when they implore my aid? Can I close my hand before misery and sickness?"

"But how can we protect our property," asked the sultan, "if any stranger may seize it on the pretext of giving it to charity? Since you have committed theft you deserve severe punishment. Choose between death and exile."

Death was hard to accept for a young woman who knew only the daybreak and its promises. But how could a daughter of the Maghrib live far from her native land? The princess finally chose death rather than exile. Allah, in order to reward her for her generous deeds, transformed her into a tree of great beauty—the almond tree which enhances our orchards.

Even in the form of a tree she still continues to distribute gifts; her flowers are the joy of spring; her fruit has a delightful taste; her oil is sweet and clean; she inspires peace and heals the troubled hearts of men.

Oum-Hani

And to every one of His creations He gave a living soul.

In the region of Chaouen, peasants would cut away slabs of rock from the flanks of the local mountain. The men were tall and strong and with each blow of their pickaxes a low moan would issue from the heart of the mountain.

Chaieb, youngest of the men, was engaged to marry his cousin, Oum-Hani, the prettiest girl of the region.

"A few more blows of the pickaxe," he said to himself, "and I will have rocks enough with which to construct a house."

Oum-Hani was sad; she knew that the mountain was a

6

living creature and that it could suffer; locked within it were mysterious beings whose vengeance was prompt and terrible.

"O my beloved," she said to Chaieb, "why do you wound the mountain? Are you not afraid of its wrath?"

The young man laughed. "The mountain is made of earth and of rocks. Metal is found in its entrails. It has no soul and it cannot suffer."

"The mountain is alive," answered the young girl, "the forest is its hair covering, the springs and rivulets are the blood of its veins, and the rocks are the bones of its body. Fear the mountain, O Chaieb!"

One day a large chunk of rock broke off from the summit of the mountain and rolled down the side, crushing everything in its path.

"Run for your lives!" cried the mountaineers. They threw down their picks and fled to the plain. Only Chaieb, constrained by destiny, hid himself in a crevice. The huge rock came to rest directly over the crevice and sealed off the entrance.

The tribesmen returned with their picks and shovels; they dug deep under the rock but could find no trace of Chaieb, living or dead.

When Oum-Hani learned of the tragedy she threw herself on the ground and wept. Her mother and sisters tried to solace her; they spoke to her of the Will of Allah, of *mektoub* ("fate") which no one could alter.

"Everyone," they said, "carries his destiny imprinted on his forehead and no man can change it."

But Oum-Hani could not be consoled. One night she became feverish; in her delirium she saw a group of mountains advancing toward her village. Some had their sides blasted away by dynamite, some were completely denuded of their trees. They came to destroy the villagers who had been so cruel to them. Oum-Hani raised her arms and implored them to spare her people.

"They do not know that you mountains are Believers," she cried out. "I know that the Prophet Jesus once heard a mountain weep with joy upon hearing the holy verses of the blessed Koran."

But the mountains continued to advance and the girl screamed with fright as they came nearer and nearer. For more than a month the young girl suffered attacks of fever followed by nightmares. One night, thinking that she was at death's door, readers of the sacred Koran surrounded her bed and recited chapters from the Holy Book. Suddenly Oum-Hani began to speak; her voice was clear and distinct.

"The mountains have promised me that I will see Chaieb once more before I die."

Oum-Hani grew better. After her illness she took a pitcher of milk, a branch of everlasting flowers, and walked toward the mountain. She climbed up the slope until she arrived at the spot where Chaieb had disappeared; there she planted a green twig and swore fidelity to her lover. She renounced all thoughts of marriage and the joys of motherhood.

"And now," she said to herself, "I shall appease the anger of the jinn."

She continued her slow, painful ascent. The summit of the mountain was covered with a thick forest gilded by the sun; the trees swayed slightly in the evening breeze. Oum-Hani, tiny and humble against the mountain peaks and the tall trees, pronounced the appropriate sacred words. After offering milk and incense, she descended to the village below. When she arrived home her mother was waiting for her in tears.

"How late you are, my daughter," she said. "You've been up on the mountain, haven't you?"

"I went to appease the anger of the jinn."

Time passed and with it passed many joys and sorrows. Those who had known Chaieb were dead. Other mountaineers came with their picks and broke off slabs of the mountain—the ever silent, ever patient mountain.

Oum-Hani had become a very old woman, but each Friday without fail she climbed the steep slope of the mountain. She carried a twig of everlasting flowers to honor the memory of Chaieb and a jug of milk for the jinn of the high peaks, the dreadful Oulad-el-Ahmar, whose feet were shaped like goat hoofs.

"O jinn of the mountain," she chanted, "I have always held you in great esteem. Let me see Chaieb once more before I die."

War came. Foreign engineers diverted rivers, blasted out great blocks of rock and opened subterranean galleries in the heart of the mountain. Tears came to Oum-Hani's eyes at the sight of the strangers—her heart was filled with a great hatred for the invaders.

"May Allah curse you," she said when she met them on her path.

One Friday as Oum-Hani was making her usual pilgrimage, she came upon a huge ditch surrounded by workmen. They had put down their tools and stood silently near some object which the old woman could not distinguish clearly. She was curious to know what had happened and tried to pass through the line of men. A Spaniard held her back gently. A Mohammedan recognized her.

"It is Mother Hani!"

They let her pass. She saw the body of a man lying outstretched. A pious hand had covered his face.

"Was there an' accident?" Oum-Hani asked in fright. She thought of the sorrow the accident would bring to his family.

"No," answered one of the workers, "it is a body we found buried here when we were digging this ditch."

Oum-Hani leaned over and uncovered the face of the corpse. It was Chaieb! By some miracle Allah had preserved him from decay. The old woman kissed his forehead with her pale lips. Then she slumped across his body never to rise again. The jinn of the mountain had answered her prayer.

The Origin of Tangier

Generations have come and gone since Allah, exalted be His name, created mankind as well as the jinn of water and of fire. The daughters of men were beautiful; the giants born to them and the jinn populated the earth and became renowned and powerful. But their pride-filled souls strayed from Allah's path and their souls were filled with thoughts of hate.

Allah, exalted be His name, seeing that the evil in men was great, said in His anger, "I will exterminate those whom I have created—I will destroy those who possess the breath of life."

Only one man, Noah the Prophet, found grace in His eyes.

Allah said to Noah, "Tell the people to mend their ways before the day of reckoning arrives."

Noah spoke to the people; he urged them to worship the Lord, for there was no other God but Allah; he feared for their fate on the Day of Judgment. In their perversity the men stopped up their ears with their fingers and continued in their sinful ways.

Allah commanded Noah to construct an ark out of cedarwood and to take his family aboard; he was also to bring one male and one female of each living creature that inhabited the earth. When the prophet had complied fully with the instructions of Allah, a great cloud spread over the world; the furious waters of a deluge rushed over the earth and destroyed life. The flood drowned birds who had hidden in the trees, cattle lowing on the farms, wild beasts in the hearts of forests, and the violent and perverse men who had given offense to their Creator by building towns with walls of bronze high on the hilltops in order to worship the sun. Thus were destroyed the men who were blind to the true doctrine.

After He had achieved His revenge, the Lord remembered Noah, his family and the animals who were in the Ark with him. A great wind swept over the face of the earth and drove back the deluge. When the water receded, the Ark came to rest atop Mount Arachi in the Atlas Mountains. Noah, ever grateful, praised the Lord. Curious to know if the waters had receded elsewhere, he opened one of the windows of the Ark and let the black crow fly out. The bird hesitated, then flew away; soon he returned.

"There is neither land nor branch of a tree where I can perch," he said.

Noah allowed seven days to go by; again he opened a window of the Ark and let out the white dove—white of plumage and of heart. The dove flew far afield. One

11

evening she came back bearing the twig of an olive tree. Again seven days passed. This time Noah sent out the brown swallow. She cut through the air with her wings, sharp as the point of a *qalan* ("quill") cut by the hand of a skillful scholar. She reached a land which was caressed by two seas and where the sky was as blue as the petals of a blue flower. The swallow remained there for about a day; at the hour when the muezzin calls men to prayer, she resumed her flight and brought Noah some clay between her dainty claws.

"El Hamdoullilah!" ("Allah be praised!") said the prophet Noah in the Arabic language. "El ma mecha ou ettin dja." ("The water is gone and the clay has remained.")

Since that day men have called this land Tindja (Tangier). It is located between the hill of Charf and the river of the same name. Its silent waters flow at the foot of an ancient city once inhabited by the heathen Chemich, or sun-worshipers.

The First Diamond

When the omnipotent Lord of the Universe created Adam, the first man, it pleased Him to teach Adam the words in Arabic which denote the heavens, the stars, the flowers, the creatures which inhabit the earth, and the many words which serve to praise the Eternal One. Adam learned these words and many others which were pronounced by the Creator.

Then Allah turned to his angels and asked them, "What are those glittering objects which I have sown in space?"

The angels did not know the answer; they knew only the ninety-nine attributes of Allah, the names of the eternal orchards of *Djenna* ("Paradise") and their bubbling springs.

"O Master of the Universe," said the angels, "we know only the words which you have taught us."

"Adam is far wiser than you," said Allah. "He knows the name of all things that are on the earth, in the profoundest depths of the ocean, and in the skies. Bow down before Adam, the father of generations to come."

All the angels obeyed the Lord's wish and bowed in humble obeisance before Adam—all except Ibliss (may Allah curse the Evil One). He raised his head proudly and spoke to the Master of the Universe in arrogant tones.

"You have created us from your light and yet you wish us to bow down before a creature who was molded from clay."

The Lord, may His name be blessed, angrily drove Ibliss from His presence.

"You are banished to wander aimlessly about the earth until that day when Azrael convokes the living and the dead unto my presence."

"O Lord," begged Ibliss, "let me die the last of all the creatures which you have created."

"So be it—only Azrael will die after you."

The Evil Spirit unfolded his huge wings; he spread an ominous shadow as he plunged earthward. He found refuge in a forest on the Atlas Mountains. Overwhelmed with grief at having lost his place in Paradise, he vowed to avenge himself on Allah. He implanted disobedience in the hearts of Adam and Eve, hate and crime in the hearts of their descendants. He sowed the air with the germs of mortal plagues and he grew venomous plants. He prodded men to stone and crucify prophets.

The children of Ibliss, however, despite the hatred they felt for the Eternal One, harbored a nostalgia which drew them to the gates of the glorious region in which the angels dwelt. Each night, hidden by shadows, they silently approached the gates of Paradise. They listened to the harmonious chanting of the angels and were overcome by a great feeling of sadness. They swore never to return to the gates, yet every night found them at the gates of Paradise like beggars at the threshold of a palace.

Hidden behind the pearl walls, they learned of all the events which were to take place on earth and the fate held in store for great sultans, dervishes and all men whose destiny is written for all eternity in Allah's book. When the first sign of dawn appeared on earth, the accursed demons quit the gates of Paradise and haunted the sleep of men, to whom they sometimes revealed what they had learned in the heavens. Thus were dreams born—some terrifying, others prophetic.

One day in eternity, the demons reported to their father, Ibliss, that they had learned an astounding piece of news: a child was born in Arabia and the angels were rejoicing in the heavens. Ibliss, full of curiosity, flew toward Paradise. Eavesdropping behind the shimmering walls, he could hear the rustle of palm leaves and the song of the fountains as they gurgled amid the flowers. The perfume of musk and a strong odor of henna scented the air. Ibliss waited patiently in the hope of hearing an angel pronounce the name of the child.

As the dawn broke, the angels began to sing:

> *Prayer and Peace be upon you*
> *O Mohammed, Prophet of Allah.*
> *Thou the greatest of all creatures*
> *Prayer and Peace be upon you*
> *O Mohammed Mustapha*
> *Prophet of Arabia!*

14

When Ibliss heard the name of the Prophet, his black wings trembled, and a tear—the first and last tear to issue out of those hate-dried eyes—fell to the earth in all its shimmering brilliance.

Thus was the first diamond created.

Satan's Mirror

During the time that our Lord Mohammed (prayer and salvation be upon him) inhabited the earth, there lived in Arabia a man of the race of Kinda named Zobeir. He married a young girl of the tribe of Koreish, named Mawyia, who was brown of visage and white of heart. They were honest and pious folk: they feared the Lord and honored His Envoy whom they knew personally. (If only we had that good fortune.)

Each morning at daybreak, Zobeir son of Nabigha rose, made his ablutions and said his prayers as is the custom among believers. Then he took some barley bread and a skin pouch filled with water and went into the forest, for he was a woodcutter. He cut cork oak and olive trees which he sawed into small pieces and sold to the people of Mecca; he cut cedar and sandalwood which he brought once a year to the market of Oqqath, which lay between Nahla and Taif.

Mawyia, like her husband, arose at dawn and said her prayers. When the sun cast a benevolent eye on the earth, Mawyia shook out the mats in her hut. Afterward she sat outside her door in the shadow of a fig tree and spun wool for her husband's garments. She worked thus until the moment when the day was split in two perfect halves. At the hour of the *Dehour* ("midday prayer"), when the shadow of the fig tree became green and when the earth was subdued by heat, Mawyia ate her midday repast, which consisted of a piece of barley bread and water. Then she continued spinning wool and doing other tasks until the close of day.

At daybreak, when the women of the village were drawing the sacred water of Zem Zem, they had high praise for Mawyia.

"She is most certainly the best of wives," they all agreed.

Zobeir, her husband, thought so too, and he did not cease to praise the daughter of Tarafa. Who could equal her in modesty, obedience, and devotion?

Each Friday our Lord Mohammed, prayer and salvation be upon him, instructed believers in the word of Allah the Exalted. He terminated his sermon with the following words:

"Don't put your faith in women, not even in the best of them, for women are less intelligent than men and know little about religion."

"O Prophet of Allah," protested Zobeir, "you speak thus because you do not know Mawyia, my wife."

The Prophet did not answer but simply smiled and the earth rejoiced in his smile.

But Satan (may Allah curse him), having heard the words of Zobeir son of Nabigha, said to himself, "Mawyia is a perfect wife because the love of Zobeir surrounds her with a fence of happiness and security. How would she react if she thought her husband were unfaithful to her? Let me think of some ruse which would put her to the test."

The Accursed One took a piece of glass, gave it the shape and brilliance of the moon, and covered one side with mercury so that it would reflect the image of whosoever looked into it.

16

Breathing upon the glass he said, "It is your duty to deceive!"

Satan then took on the appearance of an old woman and went to seek out Mawyia. The "old woman" found her sitting before her door spinning wool and singing:

> *You ask me*
> *What is love?*
> *I shall answer you*
> *Truthfully.*
> *Love is a plant*
> *With deep roots*
> *And its flower is*
> *Fidelity.*

"Greetings upon you, my daughter," said Satan the Ostrácized.

"Greetings upon you, O my ancient mother," said Mawyia and arose. "Enter my house, eat my bread, drink my water, and repose your tired body upon my mat."

Satan entered the woodcutter's hut and sat down while Mawyia gathered figs from her garden. She offered them, together with bread and water, to the guest.

"May Allah bless you," said the "old woman," feigning gratitude, "but tell me, I pray you, why is your bread cold and your water warm?"

"O my mother," answered Mawyia, "my husband is a woodcutter. He works in the sun and in the shade. His food is the bread that is chilled by the wind, his drink is the water that is warmed by the heat of the day. Should I therefore quench my thirst with fresh, cool well water and eat bread that is browned by the hot flame?"

Satan, may he be cursed, began to laugh.

"Why are you laughing?" asked the young woman.

"I am laughing at your naïveté. Listen to my words and don't be offended. The forest is not what you think it is. It has many cool arbors. The man you are sorry for is now reclining in the perfumed shade of the trees; while you are eating stale bread he is savoring delicious honey beignets [flat cakes] which have been prepared for him by a beautiful woman of his tribe—your rival."

"You're lying, old woman," said Mawyia in anger. She had never known jealousy before this. Now it struck her like a dagger.

"I am not lying, my daughter. Allah is my witness, your husband is deceiving you. He meets his gazelle on the road or deep in the forest. How many times have I seen them— she walking ahead of her lover. Her step is as light as that of the chamois, her mouth has the roundness of a precious ring, her eyes are the color of ripe olives, her cheeks are two fields of roses, her hair—but if you like I can show you her portrait, for I am skillful in the art of reproducing images of the children of Adam and all the creatures of Allah."

"Let me see her likeness," said the wife of the woodcutter.

Satan, may he be cursed, drew from the pocket of his cloak the glass which he had covered on one side with mercury and showed it to Mawyia.

"Look," he said, "how beautiful this woman is." And Mawyia saw in the mirror a face of great perfection; golden skin, a flowering mouth, two large black eyes, a high forehead that reminded one of the citadels that defend our towns.

Mawyia knew nothing of the ruses of Satan, nor that the image she saw in the mirror was her own. In those days a woman believed she could see her reflection only in the water at the bottom of a well. The poor woman began to weep and to lament her fate. She threw herself to the ground and tore her face with her nails.

His ax on his shoulder and his steps slowed by fatigue, Zobeir the woodcutter returned home and rejoiced at the thought of his wife the Koreishite.

18

"Blessed be Allah," he said, "who has given me such a wife." As he drew near his village he saw that the threshold of his house was deserted and the door was shut.

"What happened to Mawyia?" he asked himself with a trembling heart.

He pushed open the door and found his wife sitting in silence, her forehead resting in the palm of her hand.

"Greetings upon you," said Zobeir upon entering.

Mawyia did not respond to his salutation, obliging the angels to greet him in her name.

"Why don't you answer me?" asked Zobeir.

"I want a divorce," answered Mawyia.

"A divorce? But why?"

"I want a divorce," repeated the daughter of Tarafa.

"Very well, if you wish it. But first I must consult the Prophet (prayer and salvation be upon him)."

"Go, consult him. But hurry—I want to leave before nightfall."

"My wife Mawyia wants to leave me," said Zobeir to the Envoy of Allah. "What should I do?"

"Let her go, since she wishes it."

Zobeir son of Nabigha returned home with a heavy heart.

"Go in peace," he said to his wife, "the Prophet has agreed to the divorce."

"Remain in peace," replied Mawyia. "I shall seek another home."

Mawyia left the hut and the town without shedding a single tear of regret, for the fire of hate which filled her breast dried the tears in her eyes. She walked all through the night. At daybreak she finally reached a village; there she saw an old woman sitting before a nomad's tent and weeping bitterly.

"What is the matter, O my mother?" asked Mawyia. "What is the cause of your sorrow?"

19

"Alas, O my daughter! I had a clay pot that I cherished deeply. Each morning for twenty years I filled it with the milk of Nagha, my camel. This morning as I prepared to milk the beast she became frightened—in trying to get away her hoof broke the pot."

"Don't cry, O my mother, I will give you enough money to buy a much larger and much more beautiful pot."

"It won't be the same," said the old woman, and she continued to lament her loss.

Mawyia thought, "This poor woman is inconsolable because she lost a pot which is not worth a hundredth part of a dinar, and I, a Koreishite and a Believer, abandon my husband without shedding a tear."

She was ashamed of her conduct and she retraced her steps. When she got back to the hut she knocked on the door.

"O Zobeir son of Nabigha, open! I am Mawyia daughter of Tarafa."

"I cannot let you come into my house without committing a sin," said Zobeir. "I must consult the Prophet (prayer and salvation be upon him)."

"Mawyia has come back," said the woodcutter to the Envoy of the Lord. "May I let her enter my hut without committing a sin?"

"Allah is merciful. Welcome her since she has come back," answered the Prophet.

"O Prophet of Arabia," said Zobeir, "can you explain why my wife left me yesterday and has returned today?"

"Because as a woman she lacks the power of reflection. She obeys the first impulse of her heart and allows herself to be tricked by Satan, Allah curse him. Do you remember the words that I pronounce each Friday after the *hotba* ['sermon']? Don't put your faith in women, not even in the best of them."

20

Bou-Louan

Bou-Louan is one of those ancient cities which was known to the earliest inhabitants of Morocco; it is an almost forgotten town, encircled and isolated by the Oum-er-Rbia River. No longer does it worship the sun or pay homage to graven images. Ruin and solitude are its lot, for cities as well as men are victims of destiny. It was created at the command of a sultan and was later condemned to death by the very same ruler.

In the fifth year of his reign, the sultan Moulay Ismael, following the custom that a sovereign of Morocco reside in each of the great cities of his empire, moved his court and army from Fez to Marrakech. He journeyed slowly, as sultans are wont to travel, stopping in various towns along the way or setting up his tent outside of villages. He punished tribes which had rebelled against his rule; nor did he spare those tribes loyal to him from paying tribute. Wherever he stopped the local natives had to furnish food for him and for his retainers, who were as numerous as the locusts which often descend on the land and destroy the harvest and the pastures. The tribes trembled with fear when they saw the tall red hats of the royal guard coming through the high grass.

When the sultan reached Oum-er-Rbia, the "mother of pastures," he halted at the foot of a high mountain. The arrival of the sultan and his imperial court caused great consternation among the local tribesmen. For two years now the sky had been "closed"; there hadn't been a drop of rain in all that time. The locusts had eaten what had not been destroyed by the drought. The cattle had died, the silos were almost empty, and the coffers contained neither money nor gold. Now Moulay Ismael was a powerful and much-feared despot; his glory was written in blood and the doors of his capitol were adorned with the heads of those who had had the misfortune to incur his wrath.

The women of Oum-er-Rbia wept and the men looked in desperation at their scorched fields, burned by the wrath of Allah.

"Let us sacrifice a heifer before the sultan's tent," proposed the chief of the village. "In that way he will know our plight and perhaps he will have pity on us."

"There are no more heifers," answered the religious teacher of the village, "and if there were one it would not change matters. Since when do the powerful have compassion for the weak? Our misery will not move the sultan. We owe him tribute and he expects to receive it from us."

"Allah alone can save us," said the chief of the village in a trembling voice. He had a vision of his head adorning one of the sultan's gates.

A man of the tribe rose and spoke.

"We have nothing," he said, "neither gold nor money nor flocks to give to the sultan, but we have a gift which is far more valuable."

"What is this gift?" asked the astonished peasants.

"It is Halima, the daughter of Souleiman. Her beauty cannot be matched anywhere."

"Halima? Yes, she is beautiful—but would she agree to be our tribute to the sultan?"

22

"She will agree, I am sure," said the man who had first made the suggestion. Then he made his way to Souleiman's hut.

Halima was seated on the ground before her door kneading a meager biscuit of sorghum.

"May Allah come to your aid," said the tribesman.

"May Allah bless you," replied the young woman.

"Halima," continued the tribesman, "the sultan and his court are outside our village. You alone can save us from his wrath. If you refuse we are all lost."

"How can I save you? I am only a poor, ignorant peasant girl."

"We have no tribute to offer our sultan. In his anger he will slay all of us unless you find favor in his eyes."

"What must I do to find favor?"

"You will accompany us when we go to see the sultan," said the tribesman. "You will throw yourself at his feet and tell him of our misery. Perhaps Allah has bestowed this beauty upon you so that you might come to our aid in troubled times such as these."

"I will do what you ask—Allah will be with me. I am ready to die if that is my destiny."

"You will not die. You will be a protecting wing that will hide your brothers in its shadow."

When the women of the village learned that Halima consented to see the sultan, they showered her with benedictions; then each of them gave her the most precious article she possessed—a silken robe, an embroidered vest, a belt, a bracelet, a coral collar, a holy writ encased in a brooch. Then the women embraced her and wished her happiness.

The sultan sat in his tent awaiting the homage of the tribesmen of Oum-er-Rbia and was annoyed at their delay in coming.

23

"What is keeping those dogs?" he said to himself. "Why don't they bring me their tribute. Do they think that I belong to those men who can be kept waiting?"

A servant appeared. He kissed the ground before the sultan.

"Sire," he said, "a young woman wishes an audience with you."

"Who is this woman?"

"She comes from the other side of the river, from the village of Oum-er-Rbia."

The sultan hesitated; should he hear this woman out, Why had the tribesmen not come? Moved by curiosity, he commanded the servant to bring her before him. The servant left and returned a few minutes later with Halima. The young woman prostrated herself before the sultan.

"What do you wish, woman?" demanded Moulay Ismael.

Halima kissed the hem of his garment and spoke in a trembling voice.

"Sire, please show us mercy. For two years the sky has been closed above our heads. The locusts have devoured our harvests. We have neither wheat nor barley nor cattle and we are slowly dying of hunger. We are resigned to be punished for our sins, but our sadness is great that we cannot pay the tribute we owe you. However, since we do not want it to be said that our master has not received a single token of our respect, the people of my village have sent me as a gift, unworthy as it is."

The heart of the sultan was touched by Halima's great beauty, by the sweetness of her voice and the humility of her words.

"Rise," he said, "your devotion has won grace for your brothers."

The sultan loved Halima tenderly; he gave her jewels,

24

slaves, and as much land as her eye could see to the east, to the west, to the south, and to the north from whence come the cold winds of winter. To add to her happiness he decided to build a city on the Oum-er-Rbia and in the city a palace in which Halima would live, for she did not want to leave the place where she was born. Masons, carpenters, painters, plasterers and tile-setters were brought from Fez. They built a magnificent palace that had never been equaled even by the glorious princes of the Maghrib or the builders of the Andalusian marvels. Near the palace was a mosque and at the foot of the mosque was a *medersa* (Arabic university). An enclosure crowned with towers defended the palace against the rapacity of warring tribes and protected the woman who had become to the sultan more precious than life itself.

Bou-Louan became an important and famous city. Countless strangers entered through its gates—among them many scholars. Nomads planted their tents near its walls. Moulay Ismael came several times a year to pass many happy days at the side of his dear Halima; her life flowed in monotony and sadness until the day of his arrival.

"Why can I not always be with you?" asked the sultan.

Halima responded with a sigh, "My heart languishes for you. Would that I were always near you."

Thus their love, nourished by sighs and tears, grew to great proportions until it resembled a flame that nothing save death could extinguish.

One day a courier brought a message from Halima to the sultan:

"A great affliction has befallen me. Hurry if you wish to see me once more."

The sultan took off at full speed in the direction of Bou-Louan. But he arrived too late—Halima's soul was already

25

in Allah's keeping. He could only thank the Lord for permitting him to gaze once more upon the radiant image that had given him so much joy.

"Don't try to diminish my pain but turn your eyes so that I may weep for the one I have lost," he said to those who tried to console him.

After they had buried Halima and the *tolba* had pronounced the last sura, the sultan locked himself in the palace. The next day an edict was read in the mosque. The whole population of Bou-Louan was ordered to leave the city; no one was to remain within its walls—on the pain of death.

When the edict was made known, people stared at each other in disbelief; their faces became the color of a pale flame.

"Where shall we go?" they asked each other. "Who will receive us?"

Men, women, children, and cattle began to move slowly out of the city.

"The birds that leave us in the autumn follow a road traced in the sky," said the women bitterly. "A new home awaits them in their far-off destination. But as for us— toward what destination are we headed? What road has been pointed out for us to follow? We are like a group of frightened birds who cannot find their nests."

The students left their *medersa* with great sadness.

"Allah willed it," they sighed.

The wise men whose science and prayers could not save Halima followed after them. The poor left the courtyards which had sheltered them. The slaves and servants who had looked after Halima were liberated; they departed for their distant lands and none was ever seen again in Morocco. Moulay Ismael was the last to leave. His face was grave, impassive, like that of a man who is a stranger to both joy

26

and sorrow. He did not turn his head once toward the castle which had housed his love. He dug his spurs into his horse and rode off.

Only the storks remained; they stood silently atop the towers and crenelated walls of the abandoned city; never again would it be inhabited—except by the beasts of the fields and the forest. The palace built for Halima would reverberate with their cries for years to come.

"For no one is greater than Allah!"

The Legend of El-Minar

The sea is a living and throbbing thing; she has a voice and passions. Her beauty and her power of seduction have their source in mystery.

Some years ago a tall tower stood at the extreme end of Cape Marabata; the Christians called it Torre Blanquilla ("White Tower") and it was known to the Mohammedans as El-Minar. All day long the tower looked out on the sea; at night it was lulled to sleep by the murmur of the wind on the water. It was an ancient tower whose walls were covered with gnarled vines; scorpions hid between her stones, and evil jinn gathered nearby at nightfall. The gypsies, who knew about all things, said the tower was built by the Portuguese who came here to fight against the Mohammedans. The mountaineers of Andjera are better informed;

they say the tower was built by Lass el-Behar the pirate in order to hide his treasures within its walls.

Lass el-Behar came from Rabat. He was a skillful navigator, and skilled at an even more difficult art—that of commanding men. The Spaniards and Italians knew his name only too well. El-Behar's frigate was slender and light as a swallow; the oars of a hundred Christian galley slaves made it skim swiftly over the waves. The ship was greatly feared because of the valiance of her sailors and her many cannons, each different from the other, which the pirate had captured from Christian vessels of various nationalities.

Lass el-Behar was young, handsome, and brave. Many a captive Christian woman fell deeply in love with him, as did the daughters of rich and powerful Mohammedans. But he rejected the love of Christians and Mohammedans alike, for his ship meant far more to him than the beauty of women. He loved his ship, the companionship of his valiant warriors, and the glorious battles which were later to be celebrated in song and poetry. Above all it was the sea he loved; he loved her with so deep a passion that he could not live away from her, and he spoke to her as men speak to their sweethearts. His warriors would say that at the hour of prayer he would turn his eyes away from the direction of Mecca in order to gaze at the sea.

On the day of Aid el-Kbir (sheep sacrifice), Lass el-Behar, who was in the village of El-Minar with his companions-in-arms, declined to go to Tangier to hear the sermon of the cadi and to pray in the company of the devout.

"Go if you must," he said to his men. "As for me I shall rest here."

He shut himself up in his tower; from there he could contemplate the sea and the ships as they moved slowly on

28

the horizon. The *charqui,* more breeze than wind, made the water dance under the warm summer light.

"The best sermon of the cadi," thought el-Behar, "could never equal the beauty of this scene. What prayer, be it ever so perfect, could equal the sweet murmur of rippling waters? What on earth is as powerful as the sea which stretches from one shore of the world to the other? Oh, would that the waves were a woman so that I might marry her and the ocean a mosque in which I might pray."

As these thoughts were running through his mind a storm gathered in the west; it swept over the plains and the mountains and roared about the tower. The sea gulls cried out in fright and flew away; flocks of sheep ran frantically to their enclosures. The tempest lasted a day and a night.

When the wind quieted down and the sea ceased to bellow like a thousand oxen, Lass el-Behar descended from his tower. On the narrow band of sand which lay between the rocks and the water he saw a woman lying stretched out, white and cold. He approached closer.

"She must be a Christian," he said to himself, "for her hair is the color of new gold."

He lifted her up and took her in his arms.

"Perhaps she is still alive."

The woman opened her eyes; they were green eyes, green as the algae which grows in the cracks of rocks. She was a *bahria,* a jinniyeh (female genie) of the sea. Her beauty was magic and El-Behar fell madly in love with her. He neglected his warriors for her sake; he forgot his swift galley, his glory, and even his prayers to Allah.

"I love you more than anything on earth," he once said to her, "more than my life and my salvation."

During the equinox, the furious sea again hammered at the tower and threatened the village nearby. Her waters

29

mingled with those of the Charf River and even reached the gardens of Tanger el-Balia.

"The ocean is going to smash our tower," said the pirate to his beloved, "let us flee to the mountains."

"Why fear the ocean?" asked the *bahria* with a smile. "Don't you love her above all things? Aren't you constantly praising her force and her power? Don't you turn your head away from the direction of Mecca in order to gaze out at the sea? I am a daughter of the sea. I came to reward you for the love you bear her. Now the sea calls me back. Farewell, Lass el-Behar, you shall never see me again."

"Don't leave me," implored the pirate, "don't leave me, I beg of you. Without you I shall never know happiness."

"Happiness," answered the *bahria,* "belongs only to those who fear Allah and honor Him. I must leave you. I dare not disobey the voice which calls me, but you may follow me if you wish."

The jinniyeh wandered off with the tide and Lass el-Behar followed her into the murky depths of the sea. Nor was he ever seen again. He sleeps under the waves between the Tarik Mountain (Gibraltar) and Cape Tres-Forcas. He will not waken until that day when men will be judged for their actions and the earth will only be a shadow of a shadow which will finally disappear.

For Allah is the Almighty One.

The Meteorite of Torre Blanquilla

Many years ago there was a proud princess in Tangier; she swore that the only man she would marry would be one who would bring her a bouquet of stars as a dowry.

A young scholar, the *faquih* (scholar and teacher of the Koran) El-Mehdi, was in love with the princess. He had spent his life in prayer; he could make the demons do his bidding or make the earth tremble by pronouncing certain magic words. He determined to make a voyage up to the blue fields of the sky and there gather a bouquet of stars for Her Highness, the Princess. He first fasted for forty days. Then he traced a magic circle with his hands and burned white incense and gum arabic. Throwing himself upon the ground, he called to the inhabitants of the lower world and spoke to them.

"O jinn of the lower world, lend me your wings so that I may fly to the stars and to the moon and greet the sun in your name."

A jinni lent him his wings. At the hour when the sun turns a deep orange and slowly disappears behind the hills, the scholar, without daring to pronounce the name of Allah the Almighty, the Glorious One, soared into the air until he reached the fields of the sky. There the stars grew under the watchful eye of the moon. El-Mehdi gathered the stars one at a time (like a gardener who is selecting flowers for his beloved), carefully choosing the most beautiful, savoring in advance the pleasure that his gift would bring. After he put the stars together into a bouquet, he spread his wings and made his way to the earth; he followed a path of shimmering whiteness that had been traced by angels during the first days of the earth's existence. But as he approached Tangier, a strong wind rose up suddenly and blew sparks from the bouquet of stars onto his clothes. The clothes caught fire as did the borrowed wings and the scholar plummeted to earth.

On the days of the *charqui* one can still see, between the dunes and the beach, the accursed tower of El-Minar; this stone of infernal blackness is the body of the scholar, El-Mehdi, who dared to seize the stars of Allah for the love of a princess.

The Butterflies

At the beginning of the world, butterflies were flowers and not insects. Love taught them pain and also gave them wings. In the blessed Garden of Eden (*Djenna*) the roses adored Eve, the wife of Adam. They said she was the most beautiful and most perfect of creatures. They complained at not being given wings like the bee in order to follow her and brush gently against her cheeks and her golden hair. Haoua (Eve) was flattered, but she did not pay much

32

attention to the flowers; she preferred to listen to the perfidious discourse of Haia the serpent.

"Are you inferior to the angels?" asked the serpent. "Must you be satisfied simply with the beauty of a garden. There is much more to life than the bubbling of a fountain and the shade of a palm tree."

Haoua sighed; she would have liked to know life and the world. She disobeyed Allah and was condemned to leave the perfect joys of *Djenna* and to wander over the earth. When the roses learned about her fate their hearts were heavy.

"We want to share her exile," they said to the angels, "and follow her to the earth."

"You haven't committed any sins," the angels told them. "Why do you wish to leave this blessed garden?"

"Without Eve this garden is exile," they answered.

"On earth," said the angels, "you will know the cruel heat of an afternoon without shade and the biting cold of the winter."

"We will endure anything rather than live without her," said the roses with firmness.

"Follow her then, if that is your desire," said the angels.

When Haoua, sad and humiliated, went out of the gates of Eden, the roses united their petals two by two and flew about Haoua and caressed her cheeks, finally forming a crown around her head.

"We are coming with you," they cried.

Haoua did not even take notice of them, for she was thinking of the snake's words; she rejoiced at the thought that she would at last discover the world.

"We mean nothing to her," said the unhappy butterflies. "Just see how she ignores us. Now we are alone in an unknown and terrible universe with no hope of returning to Paradise."

And so the butterflies flit sadly from flower to flower.

"They are seeking someone to love," say the people. According to the angels, however, they are asking the way to the Garden of Eden.

And Allah is most learned in the Truth.

The Lizard

Once, long ago, there was a certain beautiful young woman who loved her husband deeply and expected to be loved in return, for love is a woman's whole existence. Every morning when she washed her face she pronounced the following magic formula which is supposed to render a wife lovely in the eyes of her husband:

> *I greet you, O purified countenance.*
> *You derive your beauty from Lalla Fatima,*
> *The noble daughter of the Prophet.*

One day, accompanied by her friends, she went to the bath dressed in a handsome green cloak which covered a tunic of white lace; her hands and her feet were tinted with henna and encircled with gold bracelets; a diadem was set on her forehead.

"I wear the color of hope and of the new grass, for I am indeed a happy woman," she said when her companions complimented her on the color and elegance of her dress.

But her happiness came to an abrupt end when she

34

entered her home. There she came upon her husband and her sister in a fond embrace. The young woman cried out. Her sister, far from being confused at being taken by surprise, laughed insolently.

"It is me that your husband loves," she said mockingly, "it is me he wishes he had married."

The sorrow of the young woman was so great that she asked for death in order to put an end to her suffering. Allah pardoned her sin, for it is a sin to wish for death before the time set by Him. He had pity on her and transformed her into a beautiful green and gold lizard.

Today she no longer remembers her suffering, but she has not forgotten divine clemency. Every evening at the hour of the Maghrib, when the muezzin calls to prayer, she hastens toward the mosque.

The Legend of the Stars

Chama and Noufissa were two young sisters who lived in the land of Arabia. They resembled each other so closely that the people of their village called them "Melzmin" (the two similar poles of a tent). Their father's name was Soaib. Though they were beautiful and pious, the sisters had one fault—too much pride.

Unlike other women, who boasted about their beauty or the size of their flocks, they took pride rather in the piety and virtues of their father, Soaib, and in the gift of prophecy given to him by the Lord.

"What prestige can equal our father's?" they said to their friends. "It does not come from shedding blood on the battlefield, nor from pillage, nor from wealth that is wrested by force from the helpless and the unfortunate. No, it is his wisdom, his charity, his love of mankind, and his joyful obedience to the will of the Almighty that have brought him fame."

Lalla Fatima, the noble daughter of the Prophet (prayer and salvation be upon him), said to the sisters, Chama and Noufissa, "Be modest and thank Allah for His generosity instead of being proud of something you had no hand in achieving. For the gift of prophecy, like that of poetry and beauty, is bestowed by the Generous One, may His name be praised, and does not come from any effort on the part of man."

But the young women refused to listen. With each day they were more and more proud of the virtues of Soaib, whom they loved tenderly, and they were severely afflicted by the thought that he, like all other living creatures, would one day die and leave them. They consoled themselves somewhat by the thought that he would have a tomb of sparkling whiteness shaded by palm trees, and pilgrims would gather there to pray and give offerings.

"Our father belongs to those privileged beings whose memory is cherished forever," they said, not without vanity.

The hour marked by destiny finally arrived and the soul of Soaib was recalled to the heavens. The daughters wept copious tears; they rent their clothes and tore at their faces.

"A misfortune has befallen us, a misfortune has befallen us!"

People tried to console them; one must learn to submit to the Divine Will.

36

"It is easy for others to speak of resignation and the Divine Will," said the sisters. "What would they do if they lost a father like ours? What would they do?"

Their sorrow was so great that they rebelled in their hearts against Allah; they lost their belief in the infinite bounty of the Generous One.

"What is to become of us now?" they wept.

For their immoderate sorrow, for their lack of confidence in His generosity, the Almighty turned them into stars. The two stars of equal magnitude and equal brilliance will continue to glow in the heavens until the Day of Reckoning. On that day the living and the dead will be severely judged—the sinners will moan and sigh, but the faithful will be received by angels who will say to them:

"For here is the glorious day which was promised unto you."

The Sage of Tanger el-Balia

A certain wise man in the city of Tanger el-Balia was married to a young and beautiful woman named Yamna; he loved her dearly and she loved him in return. But the sage had an insatiable thirst for knowledge; after a few months of marriage he neglected his wife and gave himself over entirely to the study of the science of Ghazes and of Ciaffar of Seville. He hoped to solve the mystery of life and death and to control the numerous spirits who inhabit

37

the four elements, for it is these spirits who exercise either a good or an evil influence on living and non-living things. He prayed, fasted, burned sandalwood and black incense. It was not long after that he felt capable of summoning the jinn of the underworld. He drew a magic circle which would protect him from the demons should they wish to do him harm. Then he drew his breath and waited. Gigantic beasts and frightful monsters paraded before the astonished scholar; there were among the jinn, however, some who were as beautiful as angels.

A jinniyeh of great beauty and intelligence taught the savant how to distinguish the spirits who appear in their true form from those who wear disguises. She explained that the former do not fear light, whereas the latter flee from it in dread. She told him about jinn who could combat the influence of the stars; of substances which make a lamp burn eternally. She taught him how to prepare an elixir which would prolong the life of a man beyond the normal span of years.

Attracted by her vast knowledge and extraordinary beauty, it was not long before the sage fell deeply in love with her. He repudiated Yamna, his wife, and kept the jinniyeh as his constant companion. Besides helping him in his study of the occult sciences, she brought him great wealth and filled his nights with joy. She gave him two handsome children and remained young and beautiful throughout the years.

Thus passed two blissful decades. But in time the sage was overcome by a vague ennui—he felt a great need for solitude. He missed the sometimes sad, sometimes gay existence of a man living among mortals. He sought out the company of other wise men or took long solitary walks.

One day, returning from a long walk in the countryside, he felt tired and stopped at the edge of a spring to drink.

In the water he saw the image of an old man with white hair and a mournful face.

"Alas, it is I," he said to himself. "How my youth has flown. Old age has placed his hand on my forehead and has turned my hair white. Soon I shall be in my tomb. I shall have to abandon Nejma and my two children. The wealth I have amassed shall mean nothing. My occult powers will not deliver me from death and the knowledge I worked so hard to gain will perish with me. My companion will continue to live on without me. Perhaps she will entice other wise men who, like myself, learned the secrets of magic. She won't mourn me. Why should she regret this doleful-looking old man whom time will quickly efface from her memory? She will never understand the sadness and the fear that death inspires. For she is a jinniyeh and will live forever, whereas I am a mortal whose days are counted parsimoniously."

He remembered Yamna, his wife. Her knowledge was limited perhaps, and her beauty was perishable, but she was a woman who could understand his fear of death, for she too was mortal. He wondered what had become of her. She had refused to accept any money from him when they had parted.

"Forget me in your happiness—but if misfortune should ever knock at your door remember that I love you," were her last words to him.

"She must certainly live in misery," thought the scholar, "if she does not already lie among the dead on the hillside."

The heart of the old man was filled with sadness and remorse as he thought of his youth, and he began to weep. He remained so long absorbed in his memories that the violet hour of sunset found him still at the edge of the spring. The young wives from the village nearby arrived in groups, laughing, singing, and clinking their bracelets. They hardly noticed the old man, for the hearts of young women are turned only in the direction of youth; they filled their water jugs and sauntered off just as they had come, laughing and singing. An old woman with sad eyes who had followed the young women to the spring approached the scholar.

"Brother, what is the matter, what is ailing you?" she asked sympathetically.

The scholar answered, "It is the weight of years which bears down on my shoulders and furrows my forehead. I regret the days that have passed and will never come again."

Having thus spoken, the old man raised his eyes and saw Yamna standing before him. It was not the Yamna of long ago with the pink cheeks of youth, but a poor woman dressed in rags and bent by life's woes.

"Yamna," said the old man in astonishment, "what are you doing here?"

"This is my native village," she answered. "I returned here when you went away. My parents died and left me a potter's wheel and the hut in which I live and in which I hope to die."

"Yamna," said the scholar humbly, "try to forget the past and allow me to come to your hut. I want to live out my last days near you so that at my death it will be your hands which will close my eyes."

"My lord, I cannot forget a past which was both sweet and cruel, but I welcome you with joy to live at my side."

The aged scholar lived on for some more years in prayer and repentance; when the angel of death finally touched him with his wing he died in peace, with the knowledge that he was loved and regretted by a sweet and modest woman for whom he had been the present and the future and all the joy and all the sadness of life.

The Algerian Bracelets

Abderrahman ben Mohammed was a boatman. He lived with his family in one of those picturesque old houses of Larache which were perched like storks on the ancient wall of the town. On one side of the wall was an equally ancient half-ruined casbah and on the other side was a castle with white towers rising high up over the sea and looking out on the sand bar of the Loukkos River. It was this sand bar that kept the Atlantic from pounding the shore of Larache in her full fury.

Abderrahman's small craft was generally moored on the left bank of the Loukkos waiting to serve the citizens of Larache who had some business on the other shore of the river. It was impossible to navigate the sand bar during a good half of the year, but on relatively calm days it was passable. Abderrahman would then attach his little boat to the port lighters which were pulled by the *Corsaire,* a sturdy tugboat; he and the others helped unload merchandise and the occasional visitors coming from Europe to the "city of vine arbors." It wasn't easy being a boatman on the Loukkos, for the treacherous sand bar sooner or later took its toll of human life. It was an awesome sight to watch the ocean waves pound the bar without mercy, then retreat only to charge again and again, drowning the sand bar in a mass of shimmering white spray.

41

But there was a good deal of activity in the port despite the difficulties encountered, and there was no lack of work. By aiding in the loading and unloading of freight and passengers from the steamships and by carrying engineers and military men to the other side of the river, *la otra banda* as it was then called, Abderrahman earned a far better living than the shore laborers; he had even succeeded in saving a few hundred duros. He led a sober life and had few wants. He had only himself to think about; his parents were living on money they had put aside for their old age. They also owned the old house on the ramparts in which they lived and a tiny hill planted with orange trees.

Abderrahman would have liked to get married, but his father thought he was still too young and he counseled him to wait a year or two.

"You will seek a wife when you have more money and sounder judgment. Don't forget, you must have your quota of wood before you can ask a girl to marry you. He who adds a day to his existence adds a year of experience."

Being an obedient son, Abderrahman always listened to his father; but when he reached his twenty-fifth year, he brought home his *faquih,* the teacher who taught him the glorious Koran, to speak to his parents. Abderrahman was determined to marry.

The young man's father and mother decided to ask for pretty Haddouch, his cousin, to be his wife. Rhama, his mother, thought Haddouch too coquettish, but indulgent Si Mohammed, his father, was sure the young girl would change with time, and that all women, young or old, liked to adorn themselves.

Rhama went to the home of her sister, Radia, the mother of Haddouch.

"I come to ask for the hand of your daughter, Haddouch, for my son."

42

Radia smiled and said, "Forgive me if I do not give you an answer, for where there is a captain the sailor does not give the commands. You shall have to ask Si Abdullah."

Haddouch, a little brunette with fiery large eyes, was in the room embroidering; feigning shyness, she suddenly dropped her work and ran into a neighbor's house. She was very happy, however, for her cousin was handsome and it was rumored that he earned a lot of money.

Si Abdullah was consulted; he reflected a moment, then said, "May Allah accord them happiness."

Rhama went home and told her husband what had transpired.

"They agree to the match," she said. "Go speak to the girl's father."

Si Mohammed washed his face, hands, and feet; he put on a new *djellaba* (hooded cloak) and the slippers he wore only on holidays and went to the home of Si Abdullah.

"I come to ask for the hand of your daughter, Haddouch, for my son, Abderrahman," he began, "so that they may marry according to the tradition of Allah and His Prophet!"

Abdullah answered with a reverent salutation. The two men then proceeded to discuss the dowry—so much to be put aside for jewelry, so much for clothes and gifts, and so much for the wedding. After coming to an agreement on money matters, they sought out the notaries and worthy men of their acquaintance who were to serve as witnesses. The group then went to the mosque where the conditions of the marriage were made known and the marriage decree pronounced.

"May Allah make the pair happy with one another," said the notaries and worthy men before they separated.

The next day Abderrahman sent his future in-laws a sheep, two sacks of wheat, and twenty duros; he sent a painted table carried by a *negafa* ("Negro servant") which held the pile of henna surmounted by an egg and the sugar, tea, and candles required for the festival. A smaller table held two tunics, a *caftan* (robe of honor) of brilliant material weighted with embroidery, a flask of rose water, and *cherbils* ("slippers") embroidered in gold for the bride, with less sumptuous ones for the women of the respective families.

Members of Lalla Radia's family and her friends prepared the flour which was to go into the couscous and cakes that were to be eaten at the marriage festival.

Each woman took a measure of wheat, brought it home, and crushed it under primitive millstones. It was a wearisome and monotonous task, generally accompanied by melancholy songs in which a human being was likened to a grain of wheat and the grinding millstone was the symbol of his ultimate fate. After the women brought the flour they had produced to Lalla Radia, they set to work making anise cakes. With firm hands they rolled, then flattened the pieces of buttered and sugared paste, and laid them out on a board covered with napkins.

On the first day of the marriage feast, Embarka, the Negress, went from house to house inviting friends and neighbors. She knocked three times at each door.

"My sisters, adorn yourselves," she said, "for Haddouch daughter of Si Abdullah is about to be married, may it please Allah!"

There was great rejoicing among the women at this news, for weddings were the only break in the monotony of their lives. It gave them an opportunity to display the jewels and clothes that were buried in their coffers.

On the morning of the second day, musicians came to play before the door of Abderrahman's house, as was the custom. When they had gone, Abderrahman, dressed in a garment of white wool, received his friends, who came to

44

wish him happiness. When the last friend had left, he decided to take a walk along the edge of the sea. As he stepped out of the door, he was met by a young girl coquettishly dressed in a *fouta* (gown) of white and blue stripes. This was Aziza, the youngest sister of Haddouch.

The girl approached Abderrahman and kissed his hand in a gesture of respect.

"My little brother," she said, "my sister asked me to tell you that her friends came to see her today. This made her very happy, but one of them said that Fatma daughter of Mahmoud was better dressed than she. Isn't the bride supposed to be more elegant than her friends?"

Abderrahman was mortified. How was it possible for a guest to be more attractive than the bride? Had he not given Haddouch two heavy gold bracelets, rings and gold earrings garnished with pearls?

Aziza went on to say that Fatma wore two large Algerian bracelets of pale gold filigree adorned with precious stones as green as the first leaves of the almond tree.

"Haddouch says that the merchant, Chloumou, has a pair just like them in his booth at the bazaar," added the girl.

The young man understood; Haddouch wanted the bracelets from Algiers. Could he refuse this request on the eve of their wedding?

Abderrahman walked through the narrow streets of the casbah with a heavy heart. He wondered how he would pay for the bracelets; all the money he had saved so carefully had been spent for the wedding celebration. But he had given his word; he would find a way.

Seated at a low table which was badly lit by a smoking oil lamp, Mohammed and Rhama waited supper for their son. Upon his arrival the mother rose and served the evening meal; a thick piquant soup, fish with olives, and roast meat. For it was a feast day, was it not? Later, when the dinner was

over, the old woman sat down near her son. She was happy
that he was being married, certainly, but she was a little
jealous of the position Haddouch would now assume in the
household. A young husband will have no thought for anyone but his bride.

When the last glass of tea had been downed and the
name of Allah invoked, Si Mohammed, who was always
sitting about and talking politics in the shops of his merchant friends, told some of the news of the day.

"The army of the Sultan, may Allah preserve the life of
our leader, has marched against the rebels," he said. The
Spanish allies had beaten Raisouli, after which General
Sylvestre gave a feast for the poor. The Christians would
now build a beautiful port; there would no longer be a
sand bar at Larache and the wives of the boatmen would be
able to sleep peacefully.

Then old Mohammed suddenly stopped talking. He
looked straight at Abderrahman as though he wanted to
say something to him but didn't know how to begin. It
was Rhama who spoke in his place.

"My son," she said, "your father and I would like to talk
to you about something important."

"What is it, my mother?"

"We want you to give up your boat and look for work
on land—with the engineer at the port. I am so unhappy
each time you cross the sand bar in that frail little boat of
yours."

Abderrahman did not answer right away; it wasn't easy
to renounce the trade which brought him his livelihood. He
reflected a moment, then turning to his father, said, "The
bar is dangerous, that's true—but I earn many duros crossing
it. How can I sell my boat now, just when I am about to be
married?"

46

"Is money more precious than your life and the peace of mind of your parents?"

"No, certainly not," answered the young man. He paused a moment, then said, "I will not cross the bar again, since you do not wish it. I will ask the engineer at the port to find me something else to do. He is a good man and he won't refuse to give me some other kind of work."

"May Allah have mercy on his parents," said Mohammed.

That night Abderrahman had a dream; he was in his boat, the engineer was beside him, and they were crossing the river at the point where it flowed into the sea.

The engineer said, "You are in danger for the last time, Abderrahman. Soon we will construct the port and the sand bar will be destroyed. She is doomed. You can hear her moans."

The young boatman raised his eyes to look at the sand bar. As he did so, a mermaid rose out of the roaring waters —a woman with eyes as clear as water and long blond hair. Her voice seemed to come from the bottom of the sea.

"I don't want to die, I don't want to die," she moaned.

Abderrahman's heart welled up in pity for her. The mermaid swam to the boat; she held out her white arms and embraced the young man. Then she drew him into the water.

"I love you, son of Adam, I have always loved you."

Abderrahman woke up. He rose trembling and repeated a number of times, "In the name of Allah the merciful, in the name of Allah the merciful . . ." Then as the dawn approached he hoisted up a bucket of water from the well and made his ablutions. Turning toward Mecca he began to pray.

Rhama, too, had risen before daybreak to prepare tea for the men. Mohammed had already gone to the mosque to pray, for like all old men he was deeply religious.

Abderrahman did not touch the little cakes that Rhama had put before him, nor did he drink his tea.

"Mother," he said, "I have just had a dream."

"It was a pleasant dream, was it not?"

"No, mother, it was an evil dream. I would like to tell you about it before I touch the food so that the dream should not come true."

"Speak, my child," said the old woman with a trembling voice.

"In my dream I saw the sand bar—a beautiful mermaid was sitting upon it. Her voice was like the voices which rise from the sea on stormy days. She wept and she called to me."

"Allah have mercy!" said Rhama.

"She called to me. Her green eyes were fixed on mine and then her arms encircled my neck."

"Bismillah!" ("In the name of Allah!") said the old woman. She rose, lifted an earthenware pot and filled it with water, then she threw a fistful of coarse salt in it, all the while murmuring a prayer.

Then she said to her son, "Come let us drive out the Evil One!"

They plunged their hands into the pot filled with salt water; then they emptied the pot into the street.

"May bad luck depart from our house and may good luck enter it."

"How happy I am that you are not going to sail your boat out on the river anymore," said Rhama, "otherwise I would die of fright after such a dream."

"Do not worry," said the boatman as he bowed down to place a respectful kiss on his mother's forehead before going out.

Rhama called after him. "Try to come home early, my son," she said. "I bought flour and honey to make beignets, because I know you like them."

"I will return early," said the young man, smiling.

Abderrahman went to the *kisaria* ("market place") where the shop of the merchant, Chloumou, was located. Despite the early hour, Chloumou, his little black skullcap perched on the back of his bald head, was examining some ancient coins which had been brought in by a woman from a country village. She had found the coins near the site of the ancient city of the sun-worshipers.

"May your day be a happy one," said Abderrahman to the merchant.

"May your morning be greeted with happiness," Chloumou answered politely. "What can I do for you at this early hour?"

"I should like a pair of Algerian bracelets, similar to those which you sold to Si Mahmoud Ettandjaoui."

"Still more jewelry after the pieces I sold you last week?" Then he paused. "The Algerian bracelets—I have just one pair left."

"Let me see them."

The jeweler took them out of a box and showed them to the young man. They were two circlets of filigree gold in which the clasps were designed in the shape of flowers. In the center of the flowers were two emeralds of a pure and deep green—like the eyes of the jinn.

"What is their price?" asked Abderrahman.

"Three hundred pesetas for you—I would ask a thousand of a Christian."

"That's a lot of money—the bracelets are so light."

"They are very beautiful. I hardly earn anything at that price." As an afterthought he added, "You won't be able to pay me all at once, will you?"

"No, I'm not rich enough to give you the whole sum."

"It doesn't matter. Take the bracelets—you will pay for them when you wish and as you wish," said Chloumou, who

49

was an honest man and knew that they had struck a fair bargain.

Abderrahman thanked him and proceeded to wrap the bracelets in his handkerchief; then, putting the handkerchief inside his shirt, he took his leave.

"Peace be upon you."

"God be with you," replied the jeweler, and added, "health and happiness be upon the one who purchases the bracelets and upon the one who is to wear them."

"Happiness and health be upon you," answered the young man.

After leaving the *kisaria,* Abderrahman went down to the port. The sea was calm; the Loukkos, swollen by recent rains, was muddy and the sand bar murmured tranquilly. The small boats rocked gently in the harbor and tugged lightly at their chains. A group of laborers were buzzing around the captain of the *Corsaire.*

"Oh, Abderrahman!" shouted the captain on seeing the boatman, "the courier is coming into port. Attach your boat to the *Corsaire* and help unload the freight—there'll be many fine duros today for a young bridegroom."

Abderrahman hesitated; he had promised his father and mother that he would never cross the treacherous sand bar again; he remembered the evil dream which had so frightened his mother. He had made a promise to his parents, true, but the bracelets for Haddouch cost three hundred pesetas! It would be better to give Chloumou a part payment now. It would be more difficult later, since he would not be earning as much by working on land, and besides, he had a wife to support.

"Wait for me!" he shouted back to the captain, "I'm coming with you."

Abderrahman put his boat into the water and attached a

cable which had been thrown to him by the men of the *Corsaire*.

The *Corsaire*, with its group of lighters and small boats in tow, made its way skillfully to the side of the steamer which had just arrived from Europe. Merchandise was unloaded into the small boats and a few passengers were put aboard the *Corsaire*.

During the procedure of loading and unloading, the weather began to change; the waves grew menacing; they broke on the shore like roaring cataracts, foam leaping high in the air like the froth of an angry monster.

"May God come to our aid," said the captain as he gave orders to his pilot to return to shore. The brave little *Corsaire*, followed by its retinue of small boats, made her way with difficulty through the high waves. She was lifted up, then pounded furiously by the roaring mass of water. She struggled vainly in her effort to advance, plunged nose-down, disappeared, reappeared, and finally crossed the sand bar—alone. The cables which had been attached to the small boats had snapped; the boats themselves had turned over or had been smashed by the mountainous waves.

All attempts at rescue were futile; the monster of the deep threw the rescue craft back on the shore and continued to bellow like a wild animal.

In the little white court, adorned with sculptured arches, old Rhama was seated on a mat before a little earthenware stove. She was frying beignets; she drew them all golden from the boiling oil, then put them on a large plate and sprinkled them with honey and orange-flower water. Ourida, the black cat, looked with longing at the plate. She hoped Rhama would be distracted by something long enough to give her a chance to enjoy this delicacy which human beings so selfishly kept to themselves.

The water gurgled gently in the great copper pot; a tray was laden with gilt-edged glasses which sparkled in the sunlight; steam rose from bowls of soup standing on the table.

Suddenly there was a loud knocking at the door. Mohammed, who was sitting in a corner praying and counting his beads, arose and opened it. Before him stood Abderrahman's employer.

"How do you do, sir," Mohammed said with timid hesitation; it was rare for an important man like the port engineer to come to the home of a man of Mohammed's station in life.

"May I come in?" asked the engineer.

"Please do."

The old man led the way into the little court. The engineer was nervous and agitated; he declined to sit down on the cushions which Rhama put before him. He stood before the two old people without uttering a word; the sight of the humble home and Abderrahman's aged parents filled him with profound pity.

"Are you looking for my son?" asked Mohammed. "He's a little late, I'm afraid."

The engineer, after many hesitations and circumlocutions, told the couple about the fate of their son—how he was drowned crossing the sand bar. He tried vainly to console them; perhaps it was the will of God—who could say?

"It's not true, it's not true!" Rhama protested. "My son is alive. He promised us he would never cross the bar again. I prepared beignets for him. He will find them still warm when he comes home."

But her voice was weak and without conviction; then she broke down and wept.

Mohammed tried to invoke the name of Allah and His Prophet. His mouth twisted, he raised his arms to the sky and then sank to the ground with a moan.

52

The body of Abderrahman was found some days later on the bank of the Arzila. His face was turned in the direction of Mecca. He had been a good son; Allah had shown him clemency by preserving his body intact—there was no sign of swelling or decay.

When the man whose work it was to wash the dead removed Abderrahman's clothing so as to envelop him in a winding sheet, he found close to the young man's heart two bracelets of pale gold adorned with emerald—two bracelets from the land of Algiers.

The Cadi and the Jewish Merchant

Toward the end of the reign of Moulay Hassan, there was a cadi whose avarice was so great that he was likened to a tomb, for the tomb, ever receiving, never gives anything back. The cadi accepted gifts from everyone but never offered the smallest sum to charity. Although he was well versed in the law of Allah, he failed to obey the precepts of the Koran, of the holy sura's. He only repeated the Chasda, for it begins with the word *la* ("no"), which he pronounced continually to refuse whatever was asked of him. The following story is told about him: One day as he was crossing the Loukkos river from Alcazar to Larache, he fell into the water and almost drowned.

A fisherman who was nearby shouted to him, "Give me your hand and I'll pull you out!"

"Give you my hand?" the cadi replied. "Never! Give me yours if you wish to save me."

One morning when the cadi was in the *Mehakma* ("Tribunal") waiting to sit in judgment over the day's lawsuits, a woman dressed in rags came before him. After kissing the ground before him, she burst into tears.

"My lord, my husband is dead and I don't have the money with which to bury him. I beg you to give me some money in the name of the Almighty, for He blesses the giving of alms and rewards the donor."

The cadi, ignoring the words in the Sacred Book which said, "Do not reprimand the pauper," became angry.

" 'Give me!' " he said, " 'give me!' Those are the only words you know. As if I were rich enough to feed all the beggars and bury all the dead of the town. Go! The men of the mosque will bury your husband."

"My lord," continued the woman, "we have no more bread in the house—my children are dying of hunger."

The cadi called the guards and ordered them to put the woman out.

A Jewish merchant of the *kisaria* was outside the Tribunal awaiting his turn to see the judge. He wore the gray cloak and the black skullcap of those who inhabit the *mellah* ("ghetto"); his heart had the whiteness of pearls and he did a good deed each day so as to find favor in the eyes of the Almighty. When he saw the poor woman being ushered out of the Tribunal, he immediately asked her the reason for the rude ejection.

"My children are hungry, for I have no bread to give them. My husband is dead and I cannot bury him because I have no money. The cadi would not help me."

The merchant was moved by the poor woman's misery.

"How much do you need to buy food for your children

and bury your late husband (may God have mercy upon him)?"

The widow mentioned a minimum sum that would cover these expenses. The merchant opened his purse and took out some silver pieces—so much to go for food for the children and the reciters of the Koran, so much to go for the burial of the deceased, and so much for the ritual alms of bread and fruit. He insisted that the woman buy her children some sweets, too. It was only just that the children of the poor as well as of the rich knew the meaning of joy.

"When you have spent all the money I have given you, ask for the home of Youssef, the Jewish merchant; there you will always find help."

During the night that followed, the cadi had a dream; he saw that dreadful place in Hell which was reserved for infidels and the unjust; the heads of the victims were covered with dark veils; their chests heaved and panted, yet they could hardly catch their breaths, like men who have been lifting heavy loads. They were allowed to drink warm water and to eat the ill-tasting fruit known as *zacoum* which grows only in the underworld. No matter how much of it was eaten, it never stilled one's hunger. The cadi saw himself among those unfortunates, moaning and repeating over and over, "If I had only known, if I had only known . . ."

Far yonder was the Paradise of Allah, land of unceasing happiness where rivers flow peaceably in the shade of palm trees. There the clouds were whiter than milk, softer than foam, and perfumed with myrtle and amber. Seated under the shadow of trees that remain ever green, the fortunate inhabitants of Heaven quench their thirst from silver goblets. Youssef, the Jewish merchant, was among them. His face radiated joy and contentment.

The cadi said to himself, "How can it be that I, a scholar

and a Believer, am condemned to inhabit the dark regions together with infidels, while that Jew, Youssef, is enjoying the delights of Paradise?"

An angel who was nearby answered him, "It was you, was it not, who robbed the orphan of his inheritance, who refused to give a helping hand to the poor? Youssef, the Jew, for whom you have contempt, succored the widow and fed the orphan."

The voice of the muezzin calling to the morning prayer awoke the cadi.

"Allah be praised," said he, "there is still time for me to earn the clemency of Heaven."

He arose, made his ablutions and prayed; then he made his way through the evil-smelling *mellah* to the home of Youssef, the merchant.

"O merchant," he said, "I was told by the guards of the Tribunal that you helped a woman of my race. It is wrong for a Mohammedan to accept alms from a Jew. Tell me how much you gave the widow and her orphans so that I may repay you."

Youssef the merchant smiled, bowed respectfully, and said, "It is useless for me to mention the sum, Sidi ['my lord'], since I don't wish to be recompensed for a single belouin which I gave in the name of Almighty God."

"And if I should offer you double or triple the alms you have given the widow and all the alms you have distributed throughout your life? . . . "

"I repeat—keep your gold, my lord. The dream you had last night was not meant for you alone—I too had the very same dream."

The Three Curses of Sidi Abderrahman of Mejdoub

Alcazar el-Kebir was a city blessed by the Almighty, hallowed be His name. The sun gave the city just the right amount of warmth and the Loukkos River generously watered her orchards without ever overflowing its banks. The fertility of the earth which surrounds Alcazar el-Kebir furnished an abundance of barley and wheat, vegetables and fruit; numerous caravans brought goods from far-off countries. Favored by Allah, laden with wealth, she was one of the pearls which were the pride of Morocco.

Unfortunately, the abundant wealth and absence of misery had hardened the hearts of its inhabitants. Occupied with amassing silver and gold, they had forgotten how to practice virtuous living, have merciful laws, or obey the precepts of the Koran; how true it is that wealth increases a man's ingratitude to the Benefactor. It could be pointed out, of course, that they had built religious sanctuaries, like the tomb of sparkling white stone dedicated to Sidi Ali Bou-Ghaleb, their protector, the mosque of Moulay Yacoub, and even a shelter for the poor and the sick. But all this was done in a spirit of ostentation and not because of any real love for Allah and His creatures.

Now it so happened that in the year of the Victory, at the end of the sacred month of Rejeb, Sidi Abderrahman of Mejdoub entered the village of Alcazar in order to rest from his journeys. He was weary from a long pilgrimage; the desert wind had cut his breath, hunger had twisted his entrails, and thirst had brought close the drums of death. During his travels he had seen the earth open up and swallow living creatures. He had marched on black pebbles as cruel to the feet as the stones that were once thrown by the Ababil birds at Abraha and his impious warriors as they set out to destroy the sacred temple of Mecca. The skin of the wanderer had become blacker and more dry than the *quaddid* (meat cut in strips and left to dry in the sun); his eyes glistened with fever. But his heart was light for he was at last in Morocco and he would soon reach his native village situated a few leagues from Alcazar.

"The Lord be praised!" he said, "this evening I will seek hospitality at the home of a local resident and tomorrow, if it please Allah, I will resume my journey."

Who would refuse to welcome the man who had been a guest of the Prophet? But the townsfolk turned their backs on him; they answered his prayers with insults; they treated him as though he were a vagabond and drove him from the city.

Sidi Abderrahman shook off the dust which blackened his feet and with the hand with which he usually gave blessings he laid a divine curse on Alcazar el-Kebir:

"May the inhabitants of Alcazar become blind because of the hardness of their hearts!"

Happily for the townsfolk, Sidi Ali Bou-Ghaleb, their guardian saint, heard the words of the pilgrim; he lifted his right hand just in time to diminish, at least in part, the effect of the curse.

"May they not lose their sight entirely but may it be impaired from now on and forevermore!"

"May they be burned by fire!" continued Sidi Abderrahman.

58

"The fire of the sun," added the saintly protector of the town.

"May the town be drowned by the waters——"

"Rain water," interceded Sidi Ali Bou-Ghaleb.

From that day on, the sun sent down oppressive heat waves. The Loukkos River, swollen by winter and spring rains, overflowed its banks and inundated the streets; houses crumbled and trees were torn out of the orchards. The swarms of flies which were born of the dirt that surrounded the ramparts of the *medina* ("city") carried a disease to the *kasri* ("shops") causing inflamed eyes and intolerable pain.

Thus did Sidi Abderrahman of Mejdoub punish the inhabitants of Alcazar for their lack of charity. And thus will be punished all those who disobey the Will of Allah, who drive away the weary traveler from their threshold, who withhold alms from the poor, and who fail to console the afflicted.

The Legend of Gold

It is said that many years ago a wise man of Cordova buried a ray of sunlight in the patio of his orange grove. He planned to dig it up after some time had elapsed, for he was convinced the sunray would turn into an ingot of gold.

—Joaquin de la Cierva

When the sun rose each morning its rays washed the earth like a luminous river. The sunlight was reflected in the waves which began to sparkle; it bathed the flowers and caressed the earth in which they grew. In the evening when the sky grew sad, when the chill winds blew and the evil demons prepared to sojourn on the earth, the sunrays returned to their father, the sun, and went to sleep on his bosom while he followed the path to the west.

Each evening the sunrays prolonged their stay on the mountain tops, for they loved the earth tenderly and only left her with regret. The earth, too, was unhappy to see the sunrays gradually disappear.

"How long are the hours of your absence and how cold is the night when you leave me," said the earth.

The sunrays answered, "Be patient—we will return tomorrow. We love you and the night is long for us when we are away from you."

60

"The night is approaching—demons will soon begin to swarm over the earth. Hurry back!" commanded the sun.

But a time came when the sunrays refused to return to their father.

"We are happy on earth," they said. "Isn't it our duty to defend her from the dangers of the night? We shall protect her from the demons which haunt the darkness."

"Obey the sun!" cried the stars. "We are here to illuminate the nights."

The sunrays answered, "Your light is weak and your sparkle is cold."

The sunrays remained on earth while their father turned his luminous face toward the west and finally disappeared after making a last appeal.

Allah punished them for their disobedience. The sunrays were to remain hidden in the earth where they would give neither warmth nor light.

"Those who will seek you out will be men of evil character," said the Lord.

"But we have no impurities in us."

"Those who will seek you out will be impure."

"We will give bread to those who suffer from hunger, we will give warmth to those who must endure the cold," retorted the sunrays.

"You will tempt men to do evil deeds."

Remaining thus in the earth, the sunrays became solidified and men called them "gold" and worshiped them. Because of gold there was hate and there was war, there was sin and there was crime. But, unto this day, those sunrays turned to gold still possess the pure light of the sun.

The Pearls

The jinn are learned and wise but they know neither pain nor tears. In the far-off land of India, the daughter of a jinni had fallen deeply in love with a mortal. The young man, on the other hand, was indifferent to her charms. Instead, he praised the grace and beauty of the women of the human race.

"They are sweet and sensitive," he said. "They have pity in their souls, for they understand sadness and sympathize with misfortune. You do not know pity—suffering is completely unknown to you and tears never dim your eyes. Love is a flower which must be watered with the dew of tears."

"What are these tears?" the jinniyeh replied. "They only redden the eyelids and dim the sight."

"You are wrong. Tears are precious—they solace the afflicted heart and contain all human joy and pain."

The jinniyeh sighed, but her eyes remained clear and free of tears.

She sought out a wise man and said to him, "I beg you to give me the precious gift of tears. I will bestow great wealth upon you and I will teach you the science of life and death."

The wise man answered, "I cannot give you tears. Tears come from sorrow and sorrow comes from the heart."

"Should I visit the saints and offer them prayers and gifts?"

"Why visit the saints? You are in love with a member of the race of Adam. He will teach you sorrow and sorrow will bring tears to your eyes."

One evening the young man she loved came to the jinniyeh as she sat at the edge of the sea.

"Tomorrow I shall marry the most beautiful and most sensitive of mortals," he said. "Farewell, *bahria,* we must never see each other again."

The jinniyeh suddenly felt an acute pain in the region of her heart and her eyes began to grow moist. She bent her face toward the water and wept. Her tears falling in the water took on the iridescent whiteness of sea foam. Her brother jinn who inhabit the depths of the ocean piously gathered the tear drops and placed them inside precious oyster shells.

Thus were the first pearls created.

Why the Bee Dies When It Stings a Human Being

At the approach of winter men sought out beehives and robbed them of their honey. The Queen of the Bees decided to go to the Prophet of Allah and complain to him that men were stealing honey from the bees and leaving the hives completely empty. Was that just?

"If a child of Adam were to die from the sting of a bee,"
thought the Queen, "it would certainly discourage men from
robbing us."

But she was so agitated and angry that she did not phrase
her sentences carefully in her speech to the Prophet of
Allah, prayer and salvation be upon him.

"Ask the Lord, I beg of you, to see to it that whenever a
bee stings a man may he die."

The Prophet of Allah petitioned the Lord as he was asked
to do. The Lord granted the request, but in these words:
"A bee must die whenever he stings a human being."

The Legend of the Monkeys

At the edge of the Red Sea there was once a city which
was called Bela by the pagans and Aila by the Mohammedans. It was a rich and beautiful city, but her inhabitants,
though they were acquainted with the laws of Allah, were
miserly and hardhearted. Like most men whose towns are
situated at the edge of the sea, they lived by fishing and by
commerce; their boats scanned the ends of the earth for
products from lands rich in gold and spices.

One day Daoud the sultan said to his people, "You
may put your boats to sea and you may throw your nets
into the water only during the first six days of the week.
You will abstain from working on the seventh day in
order to go to the mosque where you will pray to the

Lord and thank Him for His generosity. You may take an example from nature itself. In the land of Aramaia there is a river where the water flows for six days and ceases to flow on the seventh day."

The citizens of Aila soon after gathered in the market place, where they spoke against their leader.

"What does he mean by this day of rest?" they asked each other. "Must we lose a seventh part of our earnings? Who has seen the river he spoke about? Let us ignore this new law."

On the day of rest they rigged their sailing vessels in preparation for voyages to distant lands. They pushed their fishing boats into the water and scattered their nets about. But the nets became filled with seaweed and stones; not a single fish was caught that morning. The men returned home in fear. They bathed, then dressed themselves in new garments and went to the mosque. They hoped the sultan was unaware that they had worked against his wishes. But Daoud had learned of their disobedience, for nothing was hidden from him. He cursed his subjects; their bodies became covered with thick fur and they grew long tails. In short, they had become monkeys. Daoud did not take away their power of speech, however. But fearing they might be made slaves if they understood human speech, the monkeys pretended, as they do to this day, that they did not speak or understand the language of men.

The Cedar Tree of Sidi Bou-Mehada

In Bou-Zaiz (in Ait Bou-Amaran) there stood a beautiful cedar tree. It threw a shadow wide enough to shelter a shepherd and part of his flock; it offered a haven to the birds of the sky and it produced a good quantity of fruit; its fragrant oil nourished the poor of the tribe as well. The tree was so highly respected that the pious folk of the village protected it with a stone enclosure as if it were growing on the tomb of a saint.

On a terribly cold winter day many years ago when the sky was somber and everything had turned white, a peasant of the region, not having found any firewood in the forest, climbed up on the cedar tree and struck at a branch with his ax. Hardly had the metal cut into the brown bark when blood spurted in such quantity that it formed a pool at the foot of the tree. Seized by a terrible fear, the man fell from the tree and remained lying on the ground. Not a sound came out of his mouth; he couldn't cry for help or confess his sin. On the next day, woodcutters found him half-dead of cold and of fear. They burned pitch and wafted the acrid smoke under his nostrils. Little by little he regained consciousness. "Sidi Bou-Mehada" (this is the name given to the holy tree by the peasants of the region) punished the woodcutter—

he would have died but for the clemency of Allah, which is infinite.

The villagers, in order to appease the anger of the cedar tree and to show gratitude for its many gifts, sacrificed two bulls within the tree enclosure. They also offered incense, fowl, and henna. Since then, a pilgrimage is made every year in order to honor the tree.

The Owl

Years ago, when the Moors reigned over a large part of Spain, a Mohammedan warrior named Si Abdoullah ben Giaffar waged war against the infidels with the intention of converting them to Islam. One day, disguised as a beggar, he passed before the castle of the infidel king; on the parapet of a tower he saw two beautiful young women. Like all their infidel sisters, they did not veil their faces.

"Who are those young women?" he asked of an elderly Mohammedan woman who was a slave in a Christian household.

She answered, "The taller of the two, whose eyes are the color of ripe olives and whose hair is splashed with gold by the sun, is the daughter of the Christian king. The other young woman is her lady-in-waiting."

Si Abdoullah fell in love with the daughter of the

infidel king. He sent a messenger to talk to her and he put the following words in his mouth:

"Si Abdoullah would like me to tell you that he has seen you on the tower of your palace and he has fallen in love with you. What answer shall I bring back to him?"

The young woman was incensed. "I ought to denounce you to my father for daring to bring me a message from our enemy," she said to the emissary, "but I am a Christian and I will pardon you. Go tell your master that he must have made a mistake. He is in love with my lady-in-waiting. Her hair is as black as the plumes of the raven and her eyes are the color of shiny black fruit—she resembles the women of his race. Surely it is she with whom he is in love."

The messenger departed. Not long afterward he returned.

"My master insists that it is you with whom he is in love," he said to the princess. "Pray let him speak to you."

"How can I accord him this permission? He is a Moor and I am a Christian. My faith is the only true faith. Let him either renounce his faith or my love."

The daughter of the king knew of Si Abdoullah's valiance and his noble birth; his prestige was renowned throughout Spain and even in the neighboring countries. The Moors respected him and the Christians feared him. Women leaned out of their terraced windows when he passed by.

The young woman finally accorded Si Abdoullah the interview he had demanded. They met one evening at the edge of a spring in the garden of the palace. Si Abdoullah had such nobility, such tenderness of feeling that the princess could not help but fall in love with him. They met often in the royal orange gardens and their attachment for each other grew deeper and deeper.

One evening Si Abdoullah said to the princess, "I can no longer live away from you. What if your father should learn about us? Come away with me! We shall be happy in my palace. You will be my queen and everyone shall pay homage to you."

The princess was persuaded to elope with her lover. They traveled all night; at daybreak the warrior conducted his sweetheart to a grotto hidden in a mountain.

"Wait here," he said, "I shall come for you at the hour of Maghrib. It is dangerous for us to travel during the day. Someone might recognize us and denounce us to your father."

The young woman remained in the grotto a good part of the day waiting for nightfall and the arrival of her beloved.

Now the lady-in-waiting who had stood on the parapet with the princess had also become enamored of Si Abdoullah.

"If he would return my love," she thought to herself, "I would give up my race and my religion."

Great was her despair when she learned that her mistress and Si Abdoullah had run away together.

"I know how to separate them," she said to herself. "I will cast a spell over Si Abdoullah—he will forget the princess."

She cast a spell by pronouncing the magic words, "I bind you to a hundred women and one woman; to one hundred women in their light veils; to one hundred virgin slaves; to one hundred beautiful women."

The spell had no effect on the two lovers. Is there any occult power that can separate two hearts which are deeply attached to each other?

The lady-in-waiting pursued Princess Zeineb; she learned where the latter had gone and the name of the grotto in which she was hiding. Then she informed the Christian king.

"My lord," she said, "the Moor Si Abdoullah ben Giaffar has cast a spell over your daughter to make her fall in love with him. He has carried her away—she will be no more than a slave in his palace."

The king and his men scoured the country until they found the princess hidden in the grotto. The king in his fury ordered that his daughter be tortured to death.

"That is a just fate for those who betray their land and their religion," he said.

When evening fell, Si Abdoullah ben Giaffar rode on horseback across the fields in the direction of the grotto.

"Soon I will see my beloved," he said to himself. "I will present her to my mother. I will make her queen of my household."

When he got to the grotto he called out to his beloved, but there was no answer. For how could she answer when her father had taken the breath of life from her? The warrior looked through the grotto in vain. He decided to return again to the palace of the Christian king disguised as a beggar. The same Mohammedan slave-woman who had earlier identified the princess and her lady-in-waiting (when he had first spied them on the tower of the king's palace) now recounted Zeineb's fate.

"You will never see her again. Her lady-in-waiting denounced her to the king. She has been tortured to death by his orders."

Beside himself with sorrow and indignation, the warrior raised his hands to heaven and prayed.

"O you who judge and condemn! O you who do not allow treachery to go unpunished, avenge, I beg of you, the death of Zeineb, my beloved!"

Allah heard his prayer: He transformed the perfidious

lady-in-waiting into the homely owl who fills the night with a melancholy plaint and foretells evil. Every evening she flies clumsily from tree to tree or from one ancient wall to another sounding her plaint—the plaint of a scorned woman. Despite her metamorphosis and the passage of time she still remembers her love for Si Giaffar and the bitterness of his scorn. Allah, in order to punish her further, has kept her memory fresh so that she will never forget her crime.

It is thus that Allah punishes the guilty. His vengeance is terrible. May it serve as a warning to those who fear the Day of Judgment when all mankind will have to give an account of their actions on earth.

Tobacco

One day the Prophet, prayer and salvation be upon him, was walking in the countryside with some companions; they hearkened to his words and learned from his lips the path to salvation.

The winter had brought its cold winds upon the earth; the sky was mournful and the land was covered with snow. As he passed by a hedge, our Lord Mohammed noticed a snake lying between the rocks; it had become stiff with cold and there was hardly a breath of life left in it. Mohammed had pity on the snake; he bent down, picked it up, and warmed it against his bosom. When it awoke, however, it dug its sharp teeth into the hand of its benefactor.

The Prophet of Allah did not say a word, nor did he kill the perverse creature, but sucked out the poison from the wound on his hand and then spit it out on the ground. A plant grew on this spot—tobacco! The leaf has the sweetness of the Prophet's saliva and the bitterness of the snake's venom.

The Olive Tree

On each leaf of the olive tree the name of Allah is invisibly written.—From a Moroccan tale

Allah created all beings equal in perfection and beauty. He gave to all the precious gift of speech that they might know each other and learn to love one another—for hate is most often born of ignorance, and all living things are equal yet have diverse qualities which complement each other and form a harmonious ensemble. The rose is loving and sweet, the violet is modest, the cedar is hospitable, and the fig tree is generous. The olive tree is pious; he is beloved of Allah and His creatures. When the leaves of this tree move, they say, "Praise to Allah! Aren't all the creatures of the earth and sky His handiwork? And won't they all return to Him one day? One must love Allah through His creations."

One day as the olive tree looked out upon the beautiful earth he saw Haoua (Eve), the wife of Adam, conversing with the devil (may Allah curse him!).

"Do not speak with the Accursed One," said the tree. "The devil is false, he teaches the science of Harouth and Marouth—only evil can come from his words."

Hauna ignored the good counsel and continued her conversation with the devil, learning from him discontent and disobedience.

The olive tree sighed and said, "I did my best, but I have not succeeded. Allah keep the woman from the snares of Satan!"

Adam did not know that yielding to a temptress is the quickest way to Hell, for he tasted of the fruit which Eve offered him. Upon eating the fruit, Adam suddenly became aware of his nudity. He sought to flee and hide himself.

The compassionate olive tree called after him. "Don't run away, Adam. You cannot flee from destiny. It will follow you wherever you go. Confess your sin to Allah— He is great and generous. He will pardon you."

"I cannot stay," said Adam, "the needle of remorse is pricking me. I am ashamed. I want to hide myself from view."

"Go, then," said the olive tree, "for no one can stop a man who marches toward his own doom."

To recompense the tree for his love of mankind, the Lord said to him, "Your leaves will be the color of silver and emerald. Your fruit will be worth its weight in gold; flocks will hide in the shelter of your leaves; saints will repose in your shadow and they will bless you, for you are the image of abundance and peace.

The Donkey of Moulay Bou-Azza

All animals go to Paradise after their death, for they do not do evil willfully during their lifetime.—Popular Moroccan saying

Moulay Bou-Azza was a wise and pious man. He loved all the living creatures of this earth and treated them all with consideration. He owned a small gray donkey; the animal was strong, yet gentle and very intelligent. Bou-Azza was very fond of him; he would sooner confide a mission to the donkey than to many a human being.

One year (of the many years that Allah in His generosity bestows on mankind) it did not rain at all in a neighboring region. The crops were ruined and the inhabitants went hungry.

Moulay Bou-Azza called his little donkey and said to him, "No rain has fallen these many months in the land of X. The people there are suffering greatly and Moulay Ali ben Zahra, who is with them, suffers even more than they because he is unable to help them. Now our own silos are filled with wheat, and oil swells our leather jugs. Shall we leave our brothers to suffer? I will fill the baskets on your back with gifts and you will carry them to Moulay Ali ben Zahra, who will distribute them to the needy. His home is many days distance from ours and your load will be heavy. You will walk slowly and you will rest from time to time and you will quench your thirst at the river's edge which follows the road."

"I will do as you say," promised the little donkey.

The pious man put the gifts—flour, wheat, barley, and large leather casks of oil—in two large panniers which he placed on the animal's back. Then the donkey trotted off briskly in the direction of the stricken region. He hardly rested during the days and nights which followed, and he neglected to eat anything on the way, for his kind heart could not bear the thought of those living creatures in the land of X who were suffering the pangs of hunger. Only once did he stop to drink at the river's edge—as he was about to cross the river into the unhappy land of X where he was supposed to find Moulay Ali ben Zahra.

"I will rest a little farther on," he said to himself and continued his march. It was hot; the wind raised the dust of the road and burned his eyes and throat, but he continued his journey without stopping for a moment.

"Who knows," he said to himself, "someone may be dying of hunger at this very moment. Sidi Ali ben Zahra must have these gifts to succor the needy. I will stop to rest a little farther on."

The road continued like a long ribbon that appeared to have no end. The donkey was growing weaker, his strength was ebbing and he buckled under the weight of his load.

"Dear Lord," he implored, "let me arrive at my destination even though I may die immediately thereafter."

Allah, may He be exalted, heard his prayer, for no voice is ignored which calls upon Him. He granted the prayer of the poor animal and permitted him to continue until he reached the house of Moulay Ali ben Zahra. But just as he arrived at his destination he fell to the ground. Moulay Ali ben Zahra saw him from afar and ran to him. Alas, it was too late, for the little donkey was dead.

Moulay Ali dug a deep grave close to the spot where his own sanctuary would be built some day.

"You have been braver and more faithful than any man," said Moulay Ali in his funeral oration, "for what human being would have given his life as you have in order to save his fellow men. You have sacrificed yourself for those who have contempt for you and mistreat you. You will most certainly see the Paradise of Allah."

Today, the pilgrims who visit the tomb of Moulay Ali ben Zahra never forget to stop first before the tomb of the little gray donkey of Moulay Bou-Azza and there make their devotions.

The Prophet and the Gazelle

A sultan of Morocco once saw an angel in his dreams; the angel commanded him to journey to the East and receive the Law of Allah from the hands of the Prophet.

"How will I recognize the Prophet of the Lord?" asked the sultan.

"You will know him by the compassion he shows for all living creatures."

The sultan left his palace; he traveled many days over mountains and through valleys; he made his way through forests and he crossed numerous rivers. On his route he met generous, kindhearted men who gave alms to the poor with an open hand. These saints ignored their own well-being in order to minister to their less-fortunate fellow human beings. These wise men spent their days meditating about the Law of Allah. But none of these scholars could answer to the description of the Prophet of the Almighty.

At last the sultan reached the land of moving dunes, reddish sands, and violent winds which is known as Arabia. There he saw some hunters on horseback, armed with bows and arrows, giving chase to a young gazelle. Nearby a man in snow-white robes looked at the hunters with a mixture of sadness and contempt.

Gasping for breath, the gazelle kneeled down at the foot of this man and looked at him imploringly with terrified eyes. The man bent over, patted the frightened animal and reassured her. He covered her with his cloak to hide her from the cruel hunters.

The sultan knew for a certainty that here was the Envoy of Allah, for had he not shown pity for one of His lesser creatures? The sultan bowed in reverence before the man in the white robes and begged to be shown the path to Salvation.

For great is Allah the Almighty!

The Embroidered Bedaiah

Dehbia was a thin, pale young girl of twelve with blue eyes and blonde hair that revealed her Riffian ancestry. Her father, Moh, and her mother, Mennana, had originally come from Tsemsaman, in Riff territory; later they bought a small piece of clay-filled land in the Spanish zone which gave them a bare subsistence. In addition to cultivating the land, they cut down trees from the neighboring forest; from the wood they made a poor quality charcoal which they sold in the Tangier market place.

On Thursday and Sunday, the market days, they would rise early, load up their little donkey with charcoal and vegetables, and make their way to Tangier. They would go in the company of other peasants who, like themselves, led horses or donkeys laden with wood, straw, and vegetables. They would wend their way slowly through the countryside and along the river, marching through sun-gilded sand dunes until they reached the sanctuary of Sidi el-Mehfi (the unknown saint) in the Souk-Ebbarra. Here in this outer market of Tangier the peasants would spread their wares on the ground and wait patiently for the arrival of customers.

This was the unfailing routine of life that Dehbia had taken part in for as long as she could remember. She had first gone to the market on her mother's back, now she helped guide their little donkey like an expert. Then one day Spain declared war on the Riff tribes and Dehbia's world changed completely. The war did not come like a thunderbolt, but rather like the sharp crisis of a chronic malady. The men took their rifles and went to join their fellows in the Riff mountains. Dehbia's father, Moh, was killed in the early part of the war. The women continued where the men left off, guiding the plows or bending over the heavy millstones that ground the little sorgo that remained to them. On market days they would load their beasts as usual; going by devious roads they would manage to elude the Spaniards and enter Tangier.

One morning, a little before daybreak, as the peasant women marched silently toward Tangier, they were suddenly attacked by machine-gun fire. Dehbia's mother fell with the others; the screams of the wounded turned to moans and the moans to silence. Dehbia, alone unscathed, would not leave her mother's side; but the woman was still, and the wailing and tugging of the young girl could not wake her. Nor had the animals been spared, but lay in grotesque postures on the road. When some airplanes suddenly appeared in the sky, Dehbia got up and ran wildly into a nearby field to hide behind a tree. When they had disappeared, she decided to slip into Tangier rather than return home, for she knew these birds of death wouldn't drop their bombs in the International Zone. She ran through parched fields, hiding in the bushes from time to time like a frightened animal.

It was a dirty, tattered girl with tears streaming down her cheeks who stood before the tent of Rhama the seamstress. Rhama recognized the daughter of Mennana who sold charcoal and vegetables close by her tent on market days. After giving the child something to eat and to drink she began to ply her with questions. When she learned from Dehbia what had happened, she answered simply:

"The war has killed your parents—they are in the hands of Allah. You will come with me and be my apprentice. I will give you food and clothing and Allah will recompense me for the kindness I have shown to a Mohammedan child."

The next morning Dehbia, dressed in an almost new shirt and green pantaloons, took her place among the older apprentices. Rhama's little house stood in the Hauma de Benider, a native quarter of Tangier. Compared to the somber hut of her parents, it seemed like a palace to Dehbia.

However, her life was not to be that of a princess. Rising early in the morning, the little peasant girl would climb up to the terrace to water the plants that Rhama cultivated with loving care. Then she would open the window, sweep the floor, shake the Rabat rug, smooth out the wrinkles of the *telmita* ("divan cover") and put in order the cushions that the apprentices had disarranged the night before. She must not forget, of course, to wash the stove with sand and black soap. After finishing her cleaning chores, there would be the errand to the *farran* ("baker") to get an ember with which to light the little terra-cotta stove; for it was her duty also to prepare the tea for Madame Rhama before she began work every morning. At nine o'clock every morning, except holidays, the apprentices would arrive with a loud clatter of cab-cabs (wooden sandals) and the jingle of silver bracelets. Here Dehbia would join them. Squatting on a large mattress, they would sew on some pieces of material or garments which Lalla Rhama would pass out to them. Their work was interspersed with laughter, teasing, and making faces at each other. At the end of the day, the apprentices would wash down the tile of the courtyard with brushes made of dwarf palm; they made a game of the chore, splashing each other with water and shouting with laughter.

One day Dehbia was sent out to the market to buy fish, oil, tomatoes, and wheat; the girl took a large basket and set off happily; for it was a welcome chance to get away from her sewing and be out in the sunshine. The market place was at the terminus of the dirty, narrow streets of the *hauma* ("native quarter"). Dehbia was under strict orders not to tarry too long in the market place and not to cross the square which led into the European quarter. But the day was particularly beautiful and she was more restless than usual; she would think of some excuse to explain why her errand should take fifteen minutes longer than usual. After buying what she needed in the market, she crossed the square to the European quarter. The shops in the "forbidden" section were large, with wide windows. Dehbia gazed in wonderment at the lavish display of furniture, clothes and other articles. She looked with curiosity and fear at the Christian "enemy." But it was the noise and frightening speed of the motorcars, not to mention a guilty conscience, which made her glad to turn her back on the European section after lingering there for only a short while.

Once back in the market place she felt the comfort of being with her own people. She mingled happily with a throng surrounding a *hiai* ("snake charmer"). Mohammed ben Aissa, the snake charmer, was a handsome man with strong limbs and a skin that was very brown. He had two piercing black eyes which had a hypnotic quality. A white turban covered his long hair; in the folds of the turban he carried a tiny pipe for *kif* ("hashish") and a primitive flute. The gestures of Ben-Aissa were calculated and executed with great dignity; his voice was deep and rich. He did not overdo the usual invocations to the saints

81

but preferred rather to have long "conversations" with his dangerous charges. By a trick of the voice he made it seem as though the snakes themselves were speaking.

"O snake of the plains," said Mohammed ben Aissa after playing a few notes on his flute. "O snake of the woods—you who hide under rocks and in the hollows of old trees—show yourselves to the servants of Allah."

"No," said the snakes, "we don't care to show ourselves to the children of Adam, we would rather sleep."

"They don't want to come out," said the dervish to the crowd as he passed a large flat drum among the onlookers. The onlookers knew full well that only money would tempt the reptiles to appear; sous and belouins came tumbling into the drum. Then again addressing the goatskin sack which contained the adders and snakes, the snake charmer pleaded for the reticent creatures to come out.

"Come out, come out! Your master is poor—he must earn his living." Ben-Aissa then raised his arms to the sky and recited an invocation to a venerated saint. Still there was no movement in the sack.

"O creatures of Allah, the snakes must have demi-francs or they won't perform."

Several demi-francs were thrown into the drum. The dervish blew a few piercing notes on his flute. The goatskin sack began to move and the oval head of a snake appeared, followed by its long, cylindrical body; it slid out of the sack and glided slowly toward the magic circle traced by the snake charmer's wand. The snake's eyes shone with cold anger as it followed the man's movements; it rose up, poised its head menacingly, and balanced itself on its tail end. Slowly it began to sway with the rhythm of the flute. Dehbia was fascinated by what she saw; she was certain that the snake charmer was gifted with divine powers. After some moments of this weird dance, Ben-Aissa re-

82

turned the snake to its goatskin bag. He brought out others; he excited their anger, then pacified them by the inflection of his voice or the notes of his flute. He brought them close to his face and warmed them with his breath; he put them around his neck and then around his muscular arms; they dug their teeth into his flesh. Dehbia trembled with horror as if she felt those teeth on her own body. Some members of the crowd warned him to be careful; Ben-Aissa only laughed and reassured them that his patron saint, Sidi Mohammed ben Aissa, was protecting him from harm.

Dehbia was the last of the onlookers to leave after the performance was over. Much as he was occupied with his snakes, Ben-Aissa had not failed to notice the pretty girl who had watched his act with such fear and admiration. His face was kindly as he approached her and asked if he might walk with her. Nor was Dehbia in the least frightened, so gentle was his voice. He told her he was from Marrakech and had only recently come to Tangier. He asked Dehbia her name and that of her parents.

"I am Dehbia," she said, "daughter of Moh and Mennana, the Riffians. My parents are dead; they were killed by the Nessara [Christians]. I have been apprenticed two years to a seamstress in the Hauma de Benider.

"I also run errands," she added, lest he wonder what she was doing away from her work in the middle of the day. She suddenly remembered Lalla Rhama's words, warning her not to stay out too long. She excused herself and hurried away.

"What makes you so late?" said Rhama to the girl as Dehbia crossed the courtyard of the little house. "Does it take hours to buy four miserable fish, some oil and vegetables?"

"Madam——"

"Be quiet, or I'll give you a taste of the stick. Do you think I don't know what you were doing? You were probably listening to a storyteller or watching a snake charmer. You are a big girl now and you mustn't go wandering about on the streets."

Dehbia didn't answer; she put away her wooden sandals in a corner of the courtyard and began to clean the fish that she had brought from the market. Lalla Rhama lit the stove, cut the vegetables and put them on the stove to cook; then she returned to her sewing.

"Did I do the right thing to bring this child into my house?" Rhama asked herself. "She respects me, it's true— but she's too fond of the street. To control these girls from the country is like trying to put the wind in a cage. The town is full of these gazelles from the country who'll sell themselves for a franc's worth of peanuts or a lemonade. Saadia, my neighbor's little servant, ran off with a soldier—and she's only twelve years old. May Allah punish the soldier for turning the head of a poor girl. I would have done better to adopt a boy. He would have studied the great Koran; he might have become a *faquih* and made a place for me in Heaven. Dehbia will surely end up as a streetwalker."

The Aid el-Kbir was approaching. This was a highly important Moslem holiday. The seamstress set up a tent in the market place, for she hoped to sell holiday clothing to the peasants. One morning as she was arranging her stock of shirts and multicolored cloths in front of her tent, Ben-Aissa, the snake charmer, approached; he greeted her with a great show of respect. In a few direct words he introduced himself; he told her his name, that of his parents, and from where he came. Then he asked for the hand of her apprentice, Dehbia, daughter of Moh and Mennana.

84

"Allah be praised," said the good woman a little later to a neighboring vendor who sat under a large red umbrella. "At least the girl won't become a prostitute. I'm afraid of only one thing; young and pretty as she is, would she be willing to marry this Marrakechi who is practically black and much older than she?"

However, when the girl was consulted, she agreed eagerly. To her, marriage to a city man meant liberty, holidays, and beautiful clothes.

Fifteen days later, the marriage was celebrated to the sound of flute and drum. Ben-Aissa had rented a small house in the Mesalla quarter of Tangier; the house was composed of two narrow rooms, a kitchen, and a garden enclosed by a hedge. The seamstress generously furnished the little house with mats, a handsome mirror, and some dishes of green and blue design. Ben-Aissa bought a Berber rug in bright colors, two mattresses, a wool blanket, a copper chandelier, and a tray of gilt-edged glasses. Dehbia was enchanted with the newly white-washed rooms, the light kitchen, and especially the garden. She thought of planting some aromatic herbs in it—the mint and marjoram that went into Moroccan tea. One could make lots of money that way. She would also grow roses and violets to sell to the Christians, for their women liked these flowers.

There was one thing that made the new bride unhappy, however. It was her proximity to the snakes; she had a dreadful fear of them.

"Couldn't you ask someone in the market place to take care of the snakes?" she asked her husband.

"That's impossible," he answered. "They must have a great deal of attention; they have to be fed, nursed when they are sick or when they shed their skins, and they have to be wrapped in wool during the cold season. Who could do this work for me?"

85

Ben-Aissa made fun of his wife's fears, but she refused obstinately to go into the room where the hated "enemy" was kept. She lived in constant fear of their poisonous jaws, their hypnotic eyes, and their secret powers; everyone in Morocco knew that jinn hid in the bodies of snakes. One day she watched through the cracks of the door as Ben-Aissa fed his charges and put them through a rehearsal before leaving for the market place. First he untied the goatskin sack, then took up his flute and played some slow monotonous notes; this was followed by a fast, lively tune. The snakes came out of their prison and gathered around a water dish from which they drank eagerly. Having quenched their thirst, they glided in the direction of the snake charmer, for they knew he would feed them their favorite delicacies—finely ground meat, large live insects, and boiled eggs. He held the food at the end of a stick. One of the snakes tried to bite him; Ben-Aissa did not punish it but continued to tame it with infinite patience. Then he drew the reptiles to one particular spot in the room by playing very softly on the flute. The snakes raised their heads as if to listen more closely to this music which made them undulate their long, cylindrical bodies. They followed their master with eyes that were no longer angry; they began to show signs of torpor; their movements became slow, indecisive; they closed their eyes and finally became immobile. Ben-Aissa touched them with his foot, drew them near or pushed them away; he made them leap, glide, stand, and roll. After ten minutes of this lesson, Ben-Aissa put the snakes back in the goatskin sack.

"Sidi," Dehbia said to her husband later, "be careful of those accursed snakes. They bite the hand that feeds them; they abandon their eggs in the earth and devour each other."

Ben-Aissa smiled. "My holy patron protects me," he

answered. "I fear neither the snakes that crawl on the open ground nor those which hide under the rocks."

In the spring the sun warmed the snakes in the hollows where they hid; like so many of God's creatures, they went out in search of mates. It was at this time that Ben-Aissa would replenish his stock, some of his snakes having died during the winter and some others having been sold to colleagues. He filled a box with the bitter white roots of the dwarf palm and some raw meat. Then he took a heavy stick which had a hook at one end and set out for Sidi Qassem. Dehbia went with him; she adored the country-side and especially the forest of Sidi Qassem. While the young woman, more superstitious than pious, offered can-dles to Sidi Qassem, Ben-Aissa took his stick and poked the trunks of old trees and the hollows under the rocks. A sure instinct, or perhaps a particular scent perceptible only to his sharpened senses, warned him of the presence of snakes. Having found his quarry, the snake charmer fixed a piece of meat on the hooked end of the stick and poked it in the tree hollow or the rock crevice which served as a nest. He did not have long to wait. Ben-Aissa withdrew the stick with a snake clinging to the meat, now turned black. With a quick twist of the stick the snake charmer broke the creature's teeth; picking it up with the hook end he put the snake in a large tin box.

After several hours of hunting, Ben-Aissa rested at the foot of the sanctuary dedicated to Sidi Qassem. Since it was noon, Ben-Aissa and his wife prepared lunch; first they made a fire of dry branches by rubbing two stones together. It was a meal consisting of *kefta* (brochettes of chopped meat) and peppers, and finished off with glasses of mint tea. Afterward Dehbia took a siesta under an olive tree while her husband continued his hunt for snakes and

87

scorpions. He crushed two roots of the dwarf palm that he had brought and put them inside an old slipper. The fresh, bitter odor of dwarf-palm roots attracted the scorpions which are to be found in the forest. They came out of their hiding places between the rocks that surround the tomb of Sidi Qassem. As they came near the old slipper, Ben-Aissa picked them up with a tongs and put them in a large paper bag that had formerly contained sugar. When the bag was full, the couple made their way back to Tangier.

When they arrived home they were extremely tired. In fact Ben-Aissa was too tired to lock away the snakes and scorpions; he left the large tin box and the paper bag in the bedroom. He fell asleep a few moments after he lay down on the mattress. Frightened by her proximity to the snakes and scorpions, the young woman could not sleep despite her great fatigue. She thought she felt scorpion feet on her skin; she imagined that she saw the burning eyes of the snakes in the darkness. But her husband was asleep next to her, unconscious of any danger. Dehbia began to hate this man who forced her to live in constant fear. Even the neighbors wondered how she could live in the same house with snakes, and had compassion for her.

One cold winter evening the young woman warmed a brick in the stove to place in her bed. After she had warmed the bed sufficiently she crawled in under the blanket. Then, as she stretched out her legs, her feet touched something cold. She cried out and threw off the covers. Ben-Aissa hurried over to her. Drawn by the warmth of the bed, an adder had hidden under the blanket. Dehbia wept and refused to sleep in the bed even after her husband had locked up the creature. She swore that she would leave the house and go to stay with her former mistress, Rhama the seamstress, whom she should never have left in the first place. The next day she was somewhat calmer and she consented to remain in the house; but fear and resentment had killed the little love she still had for her husband.

An entire year had passed since her marriage. She began going out often without Ben-Aissa; she would often go with her neighbors to visit the cemetery of Sidi Masmoudi where the dead sleep under the protection of the holy saint; sometimes she attended marriage festivals or circumcisions.

One Friday, as part of a company of thirty women, she accompanied a bride to a prenuptial bath of purification. As she turned a corner she noticed that a young city man, dressed in fine white garments, was watching their cortege from a distance.

"That is Si Ali Cherif," said a young girl in a whisper. "He is rich and generous, but he is far too fond of women."

Dehbia was curious about the young man. Pretending to want to speak to one of her friends who stood behind her, she turned her head and let her veil drop. Si Ali saw two cheeks which were the color of mother-of-pearl, a forehead that was white and polished like new silver, two arched eyebrows in the shape of crescent moons, and two eyes the color of still water. Drawn by these charms, Si Ali followed the cortege up to the door of the ritual bath.

That evening and the day that followed he roamed the quarter trying to find out the name of the pale young woman whose image had taken hold of him.

"That must be Dehbia, the wife of the snake charmer," said an old woman whom he questioned. "She is the only one in the quarter who has pale skin and blond hair."

On the following Friday an *agouza* ("old crone") came knocking at the door of the snake charmer's home when she knew he would be out. She brought Dehbia a gold ring ornamented with an emerald as a gift from Si Ali

Cherif. She hoped the young woman would consent to an interview with him, for he had fallen deeply in love with her. Dehbia was very angry. Did Si Ali think she was one of those easy women who could be bought for a bauble? She loved her husband who was an honest and good man and did not let her want for anything. The old crone left, followed by a stream of insults.

Si Ali was not discouraged when he was told of Dehbia's anger. He sent a new *agouza;* this one had a honeyed tongue and sly ruses.

"You will present her with two gold bracelets and the ring which she refused the first time," said Si Ali.

The old woman did not offer the jewelry right away. Her approach was more subtle; she began by showering Dehbia with a profusion of compliments; she called for the benediction of Allah on the "sweet dove" whose beauty was the talk of all Tangier.

"How lovely you are to look upon," she began. "You are like the first flower of spring and the morning light. My aged eyes rejoice at the sight of your face. How can a man look at you without becoming bound to you for life? Si Ali Cherif, my neighbor, saw you walking with some other women; you were like the moon among the stars—you eclipsed them all with your grace. It was his misfortune to lay eyes on you," continued the old woman, "for since then he cannot eat or sleep and he sighs without end. Your snow-white cheeks and your smile have affected him more than any magic. He is madly in love with you. Would you let him become ill and perhaps die?"

"No, no, he mustn't die on my account," answered Dehbia, secretly flattered to have inspired such a strong passion in that young man. "But I'm an honest woman and I——"

"Of course you are," interrupted the *agouza,* "there is

90

no question about it. All that Si Ali asks is that you show yourself at the window of your room so that he may pass below it and solace his heart by gazing upon you."

"I cannot show myself at the window," said Dehbia. "The neighbors will see me and they'll surely tell my husband."

"Then perhaps you'll see the gentleman at my home?"

Dehbia at first refused; after some discussion, however, she agreed to meet Si Ali at the home of the *agouza* for a "quarter of an hour's conversation."

When the old crone had departed, after having showered Dehbia with more benedictions and compliments, the young woman found two bracelets and a ring which had been left behind; they were wrapped in a silk foulard and scented with jasmine. After admiring the objects for some length of time, she hid them in her wedding coffer. She thought of Si Cherif who had grown ill because of his love for her and had sent her such beautiful presents in exchange for a single innocent interview.

"Yasmina is right," she said to herself, "Si Ali is rich and generous."

Dehbia met the young man in a room which the old woman had rented for the occasion. She was captivated by Si Ali's respectful manners, by his words that were "more precious than pearls and finer than amber"; she accorded him many interviews and finally gave herself to him in the hope that someday she might become his wife.

"I shall be rich then," she said to herself. "I shall have slaves and jewels and my servants will address me as *lalla* ['my lady']." It flattered her to think that she, a peasant girl from the Riff mountains, was the mistress of a wealthy city man. Another motive for succumbing to Si Cherif was her hatred for Ben-Aissa; this was her revenge for living in constant terror of his snakes.

Becoming more and more imprudent as time went on, they met not only in the little room but also at Dehbia's home when the snake charmer was entertaining the crowds at the market place. Soon enough the quarter became aware of the love affair in its midst. Ben-Aissa alone seemed to know nothing about it. Distant and taciturn, disliked by his neighbors, who feared his magic powers and were sorry for his wife, he did not have a single friend who might inform him of the liaison. Dehbia and her lover were sure they had hoodwinked Ben-Aissa. However, ignorant peasant girl that she was, Dehbia was superstitious.

"The snakes are jinn," she said to Si Ali once. "They look at me as though they know I am living in sin and they are going to punish me."

Her lover reassured her that she had nothing to fear from Ben-Aissa's snakes; the snake charmer removed their fangs and broke their teeth.

"Would a jinni allow a miserable snake charmer to mistreat him like that?"

In the early part of May, Ben-Aissa went on a hunt for more scorpions. The scorpions would later be put in a jar of oil to make a remedy against falling hair. The snake charmer asked his wife to come along with him, but this time she refused.

"I'm tired," she said, "my head aches—I must lie down."

Ben-Aissa departed alone. He felt very unhappy; a change had come over Dehbia. She was always sulky and it seemed to him that his every action irritated her. A few days ago she had shouted at him in anger that he wasn't good for anything except to make snakes dance. Even the snakes were behaving strangely; they refused to obey his voice and they tried to bite him when he trained or fed them. What could he do to make Dehbia happy? Should he give up his occupation and go to work as an ordinary laborer for the Christian *mohandiz* ("engineer")?

At Sidi Qassem, the snake charmer managed to capture two dozen scorpions. He deemed that to be an ample supply and he decided to return home. It was about one o'clock in the afternoon when he passed the airfield. There he came upon one of his friends, Bou-Zian the mule drover, who was leading some mules and donkeys to the market place; Bou-Zian had stopped for a few minutes to water the animals.

"Greetings upon you," said Bou-Zian, "where are you headed for?"

"Peace be with you," answered Ben-Aissa, "I have just come from Sidi Qassem and I'm on my way back to Tangier."

"Good! Climb up on one of the mules. We will go together. Conversation will shorten the journey."

They had not seen each other for many months and there was much to talk about.

Bou-Zian was a poor man who barely made ends meet. This had not always been the case; years ago when there were no railroads or automobiles in Morocco, travelers rented horses and mules in order to go from one village to another. In those days a drover could make lots of money, and in the words of Bou-Zian, "the sons of Adam did not run the risk of being crushed like lice by horseless carriages."

Ben-Aissa arrived at Mesalla a good hour before sunset. The quarter was still flooded with sunlight. Women were coming from the bath wrapped in wool cloaks, their faces hidden by embroidered handkerchiefs. Bakers with smoke-blackened faces hurried along carrying boards laden with round breads that had just come hot from the oven; there was a strong odor of anise as they went by. The neighborhood children were playing games. An old beggar sat under an acacia tree asking for alms in the name of Moulay Abd-el-

93

Kader of Bagdad; the *baqualat* ("storekeepers") in white turbans and oil-stained blue shirts sat before their shops smoking and talking; workmen dressed in russet *djellabas* or in old military jackets were returning from the factories. They were tired, but happy to be going home.

Ben-Aissa looked at them with envy.

"Am I then the only one who returns home without joy?" he asked himself. He stopped before the door of his house; he knocked three times and waited. The courtyard was silent, the terrace was deserted, the mortar was silent in the kitchen.

"Dehbia must be sleeping or she may have gone out," Ben-Aissa reasoned. Nearby, the neighbor's little daughter was playing a children's game by herself. He called to the girl.

"Aziza, did my wife Dehbia go out?"

"No, sir," said the girl, "I didn't see her go out. She must be at home."

Again Ben-Aissa knocked—this time with his stick. Then he put his ear to the door. He thought he heard the sound of branches snapping, followed by a dull thud, then bare feet running on the tiles of the courtyard. A bolt slid back and a sleepy voice asked who it was.

"Achkoun?" ("Who is it?")

"Open!" said Ben-Aissa.

The door opened. Dehbia appeared with her hair undone and her eyes swollen with sleep.

"Did I let you wait long?" she asked her husband. "I was asleep."

"Yes, I waited a little while. I thought you were out, but Aziza said you were at home."

"How did she know?" said Dehbia. There was a momentary look of uneasiness on her face.

"She was playing in front of our garden. She would have seen you if you had gone out."

"I was asleep," repeated the young woman. "I didn't think you would be back until this evening."

Ben-Aissa put down his sack full of scorpions in the room set aside for the snakes and scorpions.

"You must have walked a lot today," Dehbia said to him. "You must be hungry."

"Yes, I am hungry," he answered, "but I didn't walk very long. I met Bou-Zian, the Marrakechi, who was going to the Tangier market. He let me ride on one of his animals."

While talking, the snake charmer took off his *djellaba* and stretched himself full length on the mattress which lay in the rear of the room; but he did not dare fall asleep, for he had not yet fed his snakes. He kept his eyes open by studying the objects in the room. He could distinguish the large brass tray as the last rays of the sun fell on it. As his eyes became more and more accustomed to the semi-darkness, he could see the gilt-edged tea glasses on the chest. Then he noticed a *bedaiah* ("vest"), decorated with lace trimming and silk buttons, hanging on a nail.

"Dehbia!" he called, "Dehbia!"

His wife hurried over to him.

"Where did that *bedaiah* come from?" Ben-Aissa asked with suspicion.

The young woman grew pale but she answered without hesitation.

"It's from my former mistress, Lalla Rhama, the dress-maker. I must change the buttons of the collar which are old and the lace which is faded."

Ben-Aissa got up and took the garment off the hook.

"The lace is faded, true. But it's an elegant *bedaiah* just the same. What fine material," he said with admiration.

95

"Give it to me!" said Dehbia, almost tearing it away from him. "Your hands are dirty."

She tried to hang the *bedaiah* back on the nail; perhaps the nail was too high for her, or perhaps in her haste she hooked it on badly, but the *bedaiah* fell down and a handful of coins tumbled out on the floor.

"Well, they forgot the money in the pockets of the *bedaiah*," said the snake charmer.

Dehbia didn't answer. She was bent over, gathering up the coins. When she had put the money back into the pockets of the *bedaiah,* she folded the garment and locked it in the chest which contained her clothes and jewels. Then without saying another word she went out of the room to prepare their evening meal.

After supper, Ben-Aissa fed and looked after his snakes. Then he closed the garden gate and locked the door of the house. After a few more minor chores he lay down beside his wife, who had preceded him to bed; she pretended to be asleep, to avoid being asked any further embarrassing questions. He tried not to wake her, but lay on his back, his large eyes peering into the darkness.

Where did that expensive-looking *bedaiah* come from? he wondered. How is it that the seamstress did not know that the pockets of the *bedaiah* were full of coins? Why was the work sent to Dehbia in the first place? Couldn't any of her apprentices sew on buttons and lace? But perhaps they had too much work on hand and Lalla Rhama had to have the work done quickly. How she tore the vest out of his grasp! Why did the neighbors always whisper as he passed? But that's because they thought snake charmers conversed with the jinn. He refused to let the thoughts in his mind lead up to a terrible conclusion. Dehbia would be insane to deceive him, he reasoned. Tangier was a small city; a liaison would be on everybody's tongue inside of a week. He realized that it was ridiculous for him to consider such a possibility.

But there was no question that his wife's attitude had changed toward him. It was all due to the snakes; she reproached him bitterly for keeping them in the house. But how could he do otherwise? Why did she marry him, a snake charmer, if she had such a violent hatred of snakes? As an orphan she could not be compelled to marry a man she did not care for. She must have been in love with him. He was still very much in love with her. He tried hard to please her by bringing her small gifts from time to time. He remembered the early days of their marriage; his little gazelle was sweet and amenable then. Later on, if it pleased Allah, when there would be more money, he would rent a large house and put his snakes in a room at the far end of the garden. He remembered that a colleague from Marrakech had promised to bring him two najas. Dehbia would never consent to stay in the house if she knew they were in the next room. The najas came from Marrakech. Marrakech—the name evoked a thousand memories; the camel caravans coming from far-off lands; La Place Djemaa el-Fna, its snake charmers and storytellers; his father bending his back over their little garden plot; their hut under the palms; his mother and his brothers.

Ben-Aissa finally fell asleep. He did not awaken until the next morning. It was a beautiful day. Dehbia was preparing tea in the kitchen; there was the sound of an asthmatic bellows and the crackling noise of burning firewood. Ben-Aissa arose, made his ablutions and had his morning tea.

"It is a good day," he said. "There will be a large crowd at the market place."

As soon as her husband departed, Dehbia put on her slippers and her veil and entered the home of her neighbor, Mammat.

"Mammat," she said, "I left a pot of beans cooking on the

97

stove. Will you be kind enough to keep an eye on it for a while. I'm going to see my foster mother in the market place —she has some sewing for me to do. I'll be back soon."

"Go in good health, my sister Dehbia, I'll watch your stove and won't let your fire die out."

"May Allah reward you," said Dehbia.

She walked slowly through the narrow streets of the quarter, her heart pounding in anticipation of her meeting with her former mistress. Could Madame Rhama be persuaded to support her story about the *bedaiah?* It was only yesterday that her lover Cherif had been with her; she trembled at the thought of the danger he had been in. Fortunately the young man was agile; he had leaped into the garden behind the wall in the nick of time. If only he had not left behind his *bedaiah;* it had almost betrayed him. If Lalla Rhama agreed to back her up, wouldn't she also be curious to know the truth about the *bedaiah?* Could she tell her foster mother that she had a lover? She might have to admit it—but she would swear by Sidi Bouarraquia, the saint, never to deceive her husband again.

"Good day. Mother Rhama," said Dehbia as she crouched under the small canvas tent which housed the seamstress and her merchandise. "May your morning be a happy one. How are you?"

"Very well, my daughter. What are you doing in the market place at so early an hour?"

"Listen to me, my mother, Ben-Aissa found a *bedaiah* of fine cloth in our house yesterday and he is very angry. Would you tell him, if he should ask you, that you sent it to me so that I might sew some new lace and buttons on it?"

"I will tell him that if you wish." Then Lalla Rhama gave the young woman a piercing look. "How did you happen to have this garment in your house?"

Dehbia felt her heart beat furiously. There was a minute's

awkward silence. She could not bring herself to tell Rhama the truth. An idea suddenly came to her.

"A neighbor asked me to change the lace on the collar."

"Well, I don't see anything wrong in that."

"No, there's nothing wrong in it, but my neighbor asked me not to tell my husband. I think she has a lover."

"She's a daughter of sin. You should tell the truth to your husband. After all, it's not you who are to blame."

"Yes, I know, but I swore by Sidi Masmoudi not to betray her."

"Listen to me, Dehbia my daughter, I agree to do what you ask of me, but I still think you should tell the truth to your husband in spite of your vow. Sidi Masmoudi was a saint, but he is dead; your husband, on the other hand, is very much alive. He is violent and vengeful like all the men of the Berber race. Don't do anything to excite his jealousy."

It was about five o'clock in the afternoon when Ben-Aissa showed off his snakes for the last time that day. To conclude his presentation, he took a fistful of dry grass out of the burlap bag in which it was kept and put it to his mouth. He blew on the grass and to the great astonishment of the spectators, the dry grass began to smoulder and burst into flame. After he had collected some more coins from the crowd, the snake charmer slung the canvas bag containing the snakes over one shoulder and the burlap bag over the other and made his way to a nearby café for a glass of mint tea.

Ben-Aissa was very tired. It was not the ordinary physical weariness he knew at the end of his work; it was rather a nervous fatigue, for he had been under exceptional strain all day. This was due to the extra care he had been forced to take in handling the dangerous najas which he had presented to the crowd for the first time. The café was empty when he entered. The proprietor treated him with deference and then went to fetch him his tea. Ben-Aissa stretched out on a mat in the farthest corner of the café. He drew a small pipe out of his voluminous turban and a small pouch which contained *kif*. As he puffed on his pipe and drank his tea, a great sense of peace pervaded his spirit. He had earned many duros; it had been a good day. He had even forgotten the incident concerning the *bedaiah* and all of his suspicions of yesterday. He closed his eyes; the effects of the *kif* were beginning to tell and soon he was fast asleep.

A little while later he was awakened by the sound of voices; he recognized Cherquaoui, the butcher, and some of his other neighbors. Their conversation was interspersed with muffled laughter. Ben-Aissa turned his head in the direction of the voices. When the snake charmer heard the word *bedaiah* repeated a few times, he raised himself on his elbow and strained to hear better what was being discussed. There was more laughter and then the voice of the baker could be heard clearly above the others.

"Ben-Aissa? No, no, no, he doesn't know anything about it. He doesn't suspect her at all. Why should he think his wife has a lover? Those who are in love wear bands around their eyes. We all know," continued the baker, "that before she was married, Dehbia was apprenticed to a seamstress in town. She went to see the woman yesterday and told her some tale that a neighbor had asked her to sew some lace on an expensive *bedaiah*."

The baker's round face beamed; he relished gossip. After taking a deep breath he went on.

"However, Ben-Aissa was supposed to believe that the *bedaiah* had been sent for repairs to Dehbia by Lalla Rhama the seamstress."

"Why couldn't she do this little bit of sewing for a neighbor?" asked one of the men in the group. "We all help each other out when we can."

"That's true," answered Cherquaoui, "but who of us has such an expensive *bedaiah?*" Then he added in a hushed, almost reverent tone, "I was told it was the most beautiful, most elegant *bedaiah* ever seen in the city of Tangier. Yards of gold and silver thread went into its making. Dehbia told Lalla Rhama that the *bedaiah* belonged to the lover of one of her neighbors."

"What neighbor?" "We are her neighbors!" "Whose wife was it?" "What's her name?" came the excited questions.

"Calm yourselves, brothers!" Cherquaoui pleaded with the agitated little group. "The story Dehbia told was a lie. Lalla Rhama only pretended to believe it. The owner of the *bedaiah* was Dehbia's own lover, Si Cherif. Has he not often been seen slipping into Ben-Aissa's house when the snake charmer was at the *souk* ['market place']?"

"How do you know the story about the *bedaiah,* Cherquaoui?" asked a skeptical voice in the group.

Ben-Aissa's heart was beating as though it would break apart. He strained very hard to hear Cherquaoui's response.

As luck would have it, the baker chose to answer the question in a half-whisper. All Ben-Aissa could hear was something about an apprentice girl who overheard the conversation between Dehbia and Lalla Rhama. The apprentice was a friend of Fatma's, the baker's own daughter——

The rest of the words were lost, or perhaps interrupted by the proprietor, who now served his guests more glasses of tea and cups of black coffee. Hearing the name Ben-Aissa, the proprietor pointed to the far corner of the room where the snake charmer lay in the darkness. The small group grew instantly silent. Cherquaoui placed a finger on his lips.

Then he rose and tiptoed quietly in Ben-Aissa's direction.

Hearing the approach of footsteps, the snake charmer closed his eyes and feigned sleep.

The baker returned to his friends. "Thank Heaven," he said in a low voice, "the snake charmer is fast asleep."

"Allah be praised" said the other. "He'd kill his wife if he knew about her affair with Si Cherif. These Berbers never forgive."

"I wouldn't blame him," said Cherquaoui wisely.

"Wife," said Ben-Aissa as he entered his home an hour later, "there were a lot of people in the market place today and a *babour* ['guide'] brought some English tourists. I earned a lot of money, so I bought honey cakes and a pound of meat. Some hot bread would go well with the meat.

Reassured by her husband's apparent good humor, Dehbia went out and returned with some bread, sugar, and tea. Then she lit the tile stove in the courtyard; she brought out metal spits on which she placed pieces of lamb. Squatting before the stove she began to turn the meat slowly over the fire.

During this time, Ben-Aissa locked up his snakes in their room, and began to sew some damaged areas of the sack in which he carried them. Although she was apparently preoccupied with the task of roasting the meat, Dehbia watched her husband's movements out of the corner of her eye. After he had finished patching the sack, she saw him go in and out of the room a number of times. She could not contain her curiosity and finally asked him if he were looking for something.

"I'm looking for the old wool blanket to cover some snakes that were brought to me from Marrakech," said Ben-Aissa.

102

"More snakes," thought Dehbia with disgust; but she said nothing so as not to anger her husband.

Dehbia had prepared a savory dinner; Ben-Aissa ate it with evident relish. He was in a very amiable mood as they finished the repast with glasses of aromatic mint tea.

Drowsy from the effects of the food, Ben-Aissa lay down to rest. Dehbia joined her husband after she had set the tea glasses back on the shelf. Lying in the darkness next to her husband, many thoughts ran through her mind. She remembered seeing a beautiful green cloak trimmed with silver which she would have liked to wear at weddings; she wondered if Si Cherif would buy it for her. But how would she explain its presence to her husband? Reluctantly she dismissed the cloak from her mind. Before long she was fast asleep.

A short while later she awakened suddenly. "Ben-Aissa!" she called. "Ben-Aissa! What's that noise?"

"What noise?"

"Listen, I think it's one of the snakes moving on the mat."

"I don't hear a thing. Go to sleep."

The noise stopped, then began again.

"Ben-Aissa!" called the young woman again. "I'm afraid —the snakes have climbed out of their sack."

"The snakes are locked up in their room—don't be afraid, Dehbia."

"Where is the noise coming from?" asked Dehbia, for again there were crackling noises on the dry mat.

"It's the mice—they're gnawing on the paper in which the meat was wrapped."

There was silence for awhile. Then Dehbia felt something stirring on the blanket. Before she could make a move to get up, a snake lunged at her and bit into her breast.

"O my mother, O Allah Almighty!" she screamed in pain

and fright. She tried with all strength to tear the snake away from her. The snake finally released its hold and slipped away with a hissing sound.

"I've been bitten!" Dehbia continued to scream as she tried to flee from the bed. But Ben-Aissa held her down.

"I'm going to die," Dehbia moaned.

The snake charmer took his wife in his arms and rocked her like a baby.

He said to her gently, "Yes, Dehbia, apple of my eye, my life, you are going to die. Before going to bed I brought the two najas from Marrakech into our room."

"Why did you do it, Ben-Aissa?"

"To punish you, Dehbia my treasure, my little gazelle. To punish you for deceiving me. Yesterday when you came to the door with your hair undone and without a sash, you had just left the arms of your lover."

"No, no, it's not true! Forgive me, beloved—it's not true —Ben-Aissa, call the neighbors—they may know some remedy."

"I can't forgive you. You are going to die—and so will I. The najas know no master; they will not spare me either."

"Help!" cried the stricken woman. Ben-Aissa placed his hand firmly on her mouth. Dehbia trembled and broke out in a cold sweat. She began to moan but after a few minutes her moans ceased; then her body shook violently; a gurgling sound issued from her throat; she stiffened and lay still.

Ben-Aissa removed his hand from her mouth and placed a kiss on the cold lips. There was a rustling noise on the mat below the bed; then came a low hissing sound. Suddenly Ben-Aissa cried out in pain.

The Legend of Sidi Ali ben Hamdouch

At the beginning of time, the earth was not illuminated in the same fashion as it is today. The eastern part of the earth was constantly bathed in sunlight; the western part lay in darkness. The inhabitants of this region did not know golden mornings, smiling fields flooded with sunlight, or purple sunsets. It was only with difficulty that they saw objects and people about them. The sky weighed down on their heads like a funeral veil, and their hearts were sad.

"Let us speak to the inhabitants of the eastern region," they said to each other. "Perhaps they will have pity on our misfortune. Charity finds favor in the eyes of Allah."

Those of the eastern region answered, "Brothers, we would be only too happy to give you some of the brilliant sunrays which gladden our hearts and make our lands fertile. But this is not in our power, for we are not angels and therefore cannot speak to the sun. Go to Sidi Ali ben Hamdouch. It is he who, by order of Allah, moves the sunrays from one country to another."

The people of the dark region of the earth spoke to Sidi ben Hamdouch and pleaded with him to alleviate their plight.

"Let us see the golden glory of the harvest at the break of day. Let us see clearly the faces of those we love."

The saint took pity on them. He rose, put on his cloak and slippers, and began the long trek to the land of shadows, to the dark region of the earth.

105

"O sun," he said to that star, "the path which I shall take is the path you will henceforth follow."

The light of the sun spread over the earth and illuminated it. Now there were mornings and evenings, daybreaks and sunsets, everywhere. Since that time, grateful mankind has called Sidi Ali ben Hamdouch the "Guide of the Sun."

And Allah is the Most Learned One!

The Origin of Prayer Beads

After the conclusion of her wedding ceremony, Lalla Fatima, the daughter of our Lord Mohammed (prayer and salvation be upon him), said to her father, "You promised me a gift—if it please you, give me a slave to wait upon me."

The Prophet answered her, "I will not give you a slave. I will give you good counsel instead. You will repeat the following prayer thirty times each day: 'May Allah be praised'; and thirty times, 'Allah is great.' Then you will conclude your prayers by reciting just once, 'There is no God but Allah!'"

Lest she recite these prayers more than the prescribed thirty times, Lalla Fatima counted a leaf of the palm tree after each prayer, but the wind stirred the leaves and she lost her count. She had to begin all over again.

Then she fixed her eyes on the high mountain tops and said "Nothing can move a mountain. That is why it is written, 'Each mountain is the pearl of a necklace.' The mountain tops will help me keep the count."

But fog covered the mountains and hid them from sight, and again Lalla Fatima lost her count.

"What shall I do?" she asked herself. Then she picked up some date pits and used them as counters for the first prayer, "Allah be praised." She then used the seeds of the castor tree for the second prayer, "Allah is great." And finally a pearl was made to serve for the terminating prayer.

And thus was created the first string of prayer beads.

The Sun and the Moon

Though the sun and the moon were in love, they were not a happy couple. The sun was jealous of the ocean which reflected his wife's image; he was jealous of the clouds which passed by, caressing her with wings as soft as down.

The moon was a coquette; she came out each night unveiled like a Christian woman.

The sun said to her, "Cover yourself with a veil, for it is the law!"

"Why should I hide my beauty?" asked the moon. "All day long you promenade about in the Universe, while I must remain hidden from view until nightfall. My only pleasure is to be admired. I shall not wear a veil."

"Very well, I'll choose another wife from among the stars," replied the sun. "The morning star, for instance— she is as pure as a dew drop at daybreak. She is as fresh as spring water and is covered with a veil of gentle mystery."

The moon had no intention of losing her brilliant husband, so she promised to wear a veil. The moon now hid her face behind the light mists which rose from the ponds in which she observed her image. She was far more beautiful and more admired than before, for she had added mystery to her charms.

Ibliss and the Peasant

A peasant of Fahs had a very pretty daughter whom he vowed to marry off only to a man who would do him a very great service. The young men of the town, each anxious to have this lovely and charming girl as his wife, made endless visits to the peasant. They came at plowing time and at harvest time, sometimes lending him their horses and their oxen, and sometimes doing heavy manual tasks themselves. To all he promised a large dowry and fine presents. Happy with the profit he made from his neighbors' work and other attentions, the peasant was in no hurry to marry off his daughter. To those who came to demand the hand of his daughter in marriage in accordance with the tradition of Allah and His Prophet (prayer and salvation be upon him), he would have the same answer:

"Wait a little longer. My daughter is too young to marry. I will let you know in proper time; your devotion will be rewarded."

The young men of the tribe continued to serve the wily peasant who profited a long time from their devotion to his daughter.

Now it once happened that Allah refused to send down rain to the parched earth. In Tangier the religious brotherhoods marched through the streets with banners, and offered prayers. The members of the Jewish community raised their voices to heaven by order of the pasha. But it was all in vain.

The Mohammedan children sang, "The ear of corn is parched, give it drink, O our Master. The leaves of the bean are drooping. O Allah, cover it with mist so that the widow can eat, so that the orphan may live!"

The sky was completely clear without a single cloud; its emerald color did not presage anything favorable. The thatch roofs on stables and huts were so dry that they would often catch fire and burn. The harvest was scorched and the cattle were dying of thirst.

"Alas," said the peasant in despair, "there's no more wheat in my silos; my wells are dry and my oxen are dying for lack of water. Soon I will have no food for myself or my child."

One day he came home from his fields to find a stranger at his door.

"What do you want here?" asked the peasant with suspicion, for at that time there were many cattle thieves about and a week didn't pass without a theft being committed.

"I want to talk to the master of the house," answered the stranger, who was young and handsome and spoke in the tongue of a student.

"What do you wish to speak to him about?"

"I want to work for him," said the stranger, "for I am poor and it is well known that the master of this house has great wealth."

"I am the person you are looking for," said the peasant, "but alas, I can give you no work, for times are hard and Allah has refused us rain because of our sins."

"Don't you need anyone to look after your flocks and to lead them to pasture? I will be content with very little if you will but allow me to serve you."

"Where am I to find green pastures for the sheep and

109

cows? The grass is yellow and dry. The earth is harder than the rocks on the mountains."

"Farmer," said the stranger, "it is said that you have a daughter of great beauty. Will you give her to me in marriage if by tomorrow, at the first cry of the muezzin, the river overflows its banks?"

"I swear it on my head and my heart," said the peasant. "I swear it by the truth of Sidi Bouarraquia. I will gladly give you my daughter."

"I will come tomorrow," said the young man and took his leave.

The peasant sat down near the door of his house; although it was late in autumn, it continued to be warm during the day and the people looked forward to the cool night air. From the interior of the hut came the voice of Daouia, the peasant's daughter, calling her father to come in to dinner. Just as the old man entered his hut, lightning flashed on the far-off horizon—there where the sky descends to kiss the earth.

Daouia put before her father a bowl of spiced bean soup, olives, black bread, and milk. As she was about to fill his glass with tea, a knock was heard at the door of the cabin.

"Who is there?" asked Daouia.

"A servant of Allah!"

A young man wearing a white *djellaba* and heavy beads, the costume of a Moroccan student, stood at the threshold. As he entered, he greeted the peasant and his daughter with pious salutations.

"It is raining behind the mountains," he said. "The storm will soon reach here. I have come to ask your hospitality in the name of Allah."

"Welcome," said the peasant, "for you bear good tidings."

He asked the young man to sit down beside him on the

110

mat, he gave him some bread and soup; later there was milk, butter, and honey. The host began to question his guest. From whence had he come? Where was he going?

"I come from Tangier and I am going to Fez to study the knowledge and wisdom which is taught there. I left Tangier early this morning and had hoped to cross the river by this evening."

While the student dined and discoursed with the peasant, the rain began to fall in torrents, inundating the court and washing the terraces. The good odor of wet earth filled the cabin. The oxen lowed in the stable, the horses whinnied happily, and some sheep, frightened by the noise of the storm, escaped from the *marrah* ("sheep enclosure") and ran into the stable bleating with fright.

"May the name of Allah be exalted!" said the student. "His generosity does not forget the grass in the meadow or the beasts in the field."

"Allah be praised——" began the peasant, but he did not have time to finish the sentence, for a clap of thunder which sounded like the voice of a hundred cannons shook the house. Then a strong odor of sulphur pervaded the room.

"In the name of Allah the Merciful," murmured Daouia, trembling. "The fire of the sky has fallen on the tomb of a saint."

"It has struck the tomb of a saint," repeated the peasant and his heart was filled with fright.

"The thunder roared when you pronounced the name of Allah," said the student. "O my host, might you have committed a grave sin?"

"Listen carefully and be the judge," said the peasant. "In the early part of the evening, when I was returning from the field, I met a stranger at my door. He asked me for work, but I could give him none because of the drought. He assured me, however, that if I gave him my daughter in

111

marriage he would make the river overflow her banks tomorrow at the first cry of the muezzin."

"What did the stranger look like?" asked the student.

"He was pale and handsome with a sad expression," said Daouia.

"It was Ibliss! May Allah curse him," said the student.

"In the name of Allah the Merciful!"

The rain fell in torrents on the parched earth, which greedily soaked up the water. The bed of the river was rapidly filling and soon would overflow its banks.

"I swore to Satan by the truths of Sidi Bouarraquia that I would give him my daughter," moaned the peasant. "O scholar, must I honor an oath given in ignorance?"

"You must."

"Save me, O student!" begged the girl. "I have given no promise to Ibliss."

"Did Ibliss say that the banks of the river would overflow tomorrow at the first call of the muezzin?"

"Yes, that's just what he said."

"Very well, then, if the muezzin calls to prayer before the river overflows its banks you will be released from your promise."

"But the morning is far off and the river must be filling up fast," said the peasant gloomily. "It won't wait until tomorrow to overflow its banks."

"Allah is almighty," said the student and raised his hands in prayer.

A pale light, feeble as a ray of moonlight, rose behind the mountains; as it grew brighter it painted everything in purple and gold.

The cocks of the village began to crow, "Allah brings the day! Allah brings the day!"

Awakened by the crowing and believing the morning had

112

already come, the muezzin climbed to the top of his minaret and called the Faithful to prayer.

"The night with its shadows disappears; the day appears in glorious light. Come to prayer, come to prayer!" intoned the muezzin.

Though the river was swollen by the rain, not a drop overflowed its banks. Ibliss had lost the bargain. Furious, he made a great outcry and fled into the night which once again descended upon the earth.

The student married Daouia, the daughter of the peasant; he brought her to Fez where he continued to study divine knowledge and in time became a great scholar.

Allah is learned in the Truth. He is the Heaven and the Refuge. Glory to Allah, exalted be His name!

Be Resigned to Your Fate If You Would Please Allah

Do not add to the tears you have already shed, for they are as drops of hot lead falling on the hearts of the deceased.

Madame Zahour, the wife of the *faquih* of Mgoga, had lost her two children. She mourned them a great deal and carefully guarded their clothes in her marriage coffer instead of distributing them to the children of the poor. She could not obliterate from her memory the two she had lost,

113

although other children had been born to her since. When she fondled these others it only served to bring tears to her eyes.

"If I could only see those dear little ones again. If I could only fondle them once more—even in a dream," she said, thus protesting the Will of Allah, who had taken them from her.

Time passed with the speed of a rapid flowing river and disappeared into eternity just as water is absorbed into sand. Zahour became an old woman. One night in a dream she saw the two children who had died. They were in a large garden full of beautiful flowers; the sun shone brilliantly overhead.

Weeping, Zahour called to them, "O my children, did you forget your mother? Why have you never come to console me?"

"You weep too much," they answered her, "and each of your tears swells the river which separates the living from the dead."

"Should we not mourn our dead? Did not our Lord Mohammed, prayer and salvation be upon him, lament the son who was taken from him?"

"Yes, his sorrow was great," answered the children. "But he was resigned to the Will of the Almighty."

"Will I ever see you again?" asked Zahour.

"We will see each other often, Mother. But you too must be resigned to the Will of Allah, exalted be His name. We have come back to you and we shall never leave you."

From that time on, the wife of the *faquih* of Mgoga watched the waters of the river which separates the living from the dead recede until at last she could cross it and remain forever with her children.

114

Mother, Mother . . .

In the name of Allah, may salvation and prayer be upon the Prophet of our Lord, Amen.

There was once a poor woman who had a child who was all her joy and all her sadness. She taught him the laws of Allah and she also taught him a trade. When he was twenty years old she said to him:

"My son, the time has come for you to take a wife."

"Why must I marry?" asked the son. "Aren't we happy, you and I? Why do we need a stranger here?"

The mother found a young and pretty wife for her son and gave her the best room in the house, keeping the smallest for herself.

"At least I shall be near you," she said to her son.

The young wife was jealous of her husband's affection for his mother.

"Why do you let that old woman stand between us?" she said. "Her sad expression depresses me. I don't dare laugh or joke in her presence. Let her take her meals in her own room."

The young man said to his mother in indignation, "The woman you have found for me has a cruel heart. She cannot bear your presence at the table. She wants you to take your meals in your room."

"Your wife is right. She is young—laughter and joy are made for her. From now on I shall eat in my room."

The son wept but he did not dissuade her, for he was a weakling and did not dare displease his wife.

Some time later the young wife said to her husband, "A child will soon be added to our household. One room won't be enough for us. Tell your mother to find lodgings elsewhere."

"Mother," said the irate young man, "the wife you have given me is cruel of heart—she says we need your room and demands that you leave us."

The mother replied, "Your wife is right. You will be too crowded in one room with a small child. I shall go to live with my sister."

The son wept but he did not dissuade his mother from leaving.

When the mother had left the house, the wife said to her husband:

"I am very ill. A pain is going through my heart like a dagger. I am sure your child will never be born."

"Speak no evil. May your words go to the bottom of the sea," said the husband. "What ails you? Shall I call a wise man? Do you want to visit a holy saint?"

"I had a dream," she answered, "and in the dream I was told that I must have the liver from your mother's body."

The son sought out his mother.

"Mother," he said, "the wife you have given me has a cruel heart. She insists that she must eat your liver in order to save her life and that of the unborn child."

"Your wife is right. She still has many years before her. The child has not yet come into the world. Will you let them die just to spare your old mother the few years left to her? Take the knife and kill me!"

The son refused to do so and left his mother's house in tears. Upon entering his home he found his wife twisting and turning in frightful convulsions.

116

"Go away," she said. "Soon you will have neither wife nor child."

The son went back to his mother's house. There he slew her and placed her liver on a platter. Then as he made his way back to his home he accidentally stubbed his toe against a rock.

His mother's liver asked, "Are you hurt, my child?"

Quinza the Hairdresser

The daughter of the Christian king was exceedingly beautiful. She took pleasure in wearing rich garments and jewels and in perfuming herself with unguents and balms. She had a retinue of Negro slaves and white servants to do her bidding, among which was Quinza the hairdresser. Quinza was a Mohammedan, for she followed in the ways of Allah, whereas the other servants and slaves were heathens who worshiped images of stone and metal.

One day as the hairdresser was passing a comb scented with jasmine through the princess's hair, the latter made a sudden move and the comb fell to the ground but did not break.

"Our Lord be praised!" said the hairdresser as she stooped to pick up the comb.

"It is good of you to praise my father," observed the princess.

"No, I praise Him who is master of all of us and is your father's master as well," answered the servant, "for all the creatures of the sky, the land, and the water owe him their allegiance."

"Your words are disloyal—I shall tell my father."

"Do as you wish, my lady, I cannot speak otherwise."

Having been informed of Quinza's words, the king sent two guards to fetch her and her children.

"The king would have you come before him," they said.

"I am ready."

When she appeared before the king, he asked her, "Who is your master, woman, if not I? Tell me."

"He is the Lord of Mankind. He is your master and mine," Quinza answered.

The king ordered his guards to throw the woman's children one by one into a large bronze oven; Quinza herself was to be put in the oven last. The men obeyed, for their hearts, like that of their master, were cruel and knew no pity.

When the children were seized they began to sing, and after they were thrown into the furnace, their flesh gave forth the odor of jasmine and rose.

Quinza fell at the feet of the king.

"Grant me one wish, I beg of you!"

"Speak," answered the king, "you have been a faithful servant up to now."

"After our flesh is burned away, please bury our bones in the fresh earth."

"It will be done."

Quinza, like her children, was thrown into the furnace and there died in torment. Her bones were buried in the earth together with those of her children as she had requested.

The name of Quinza the hairdresser was forgotten upon the earth, for it is said, "The memory of the mad is short and that of the just is effaced like a shadow in the light of the sun." But Allah in His generosity recompensed the woman for her faith and her martyrdom; she was turned into a constellation of the heavens—Nah, the Chariot, which never passes below the horizon and whose two most brilliant stars lie in a straight line with Nejm el-Ktad, the star of the navigators.

Thus are rewarded those who have no fear in proclaiming their faith in the religion of Islam.

The Birds of the Prophet

One day when Mohammed was a small child, he and his foster brother Masrouk wandered away from the tent of Hlima, the wet nurse, in order to play games. They wandered far from the encampment and almost died of thirst. Masrouk, who was the taller and the stronger of the two, spoke to our Lord Mohammed (prayer and salvation be upon him).

"O my brother," he said, "you must not walk any farther, for you are tormented by thirst. Wait here and I will look for help."

Sidna Mohammed remained alone. A violent wind rose up and sand began to rain down upon his head. Little by little he was being buried alive. Swallows coming from Egypt recognized the child Mohammed. Descending from the clouds, they greeted him with reverent bows.

"Greetings upon you, O Mohammed," they said, "blessings upon the Prophet of Arabia!"

The child did not respond to their salutations; his eyes

were closed and his mouth was dry and burning—he was waiting for death.

Now it is known that Houteifa the swallow, through the wisdom of his instinct, never migrates across the desert without first taking a drop of water in his beak. The birds who greeted the Prophet of Allah brought their beaks close to the face of the Holiest of Creatures and moistened his lips with a drop of cold dew—the wind of the high regions of the sky had made it as cold as snow. As they came close to Sidna Mohammed, their breasts touched the face of the Predestined One; from that moment until this day, the swallow's breast is of a pure white hue.

The Water-Carrier

Water given as alms deserves the benediction of Allah.

El-Arbi was a poor water-carrier. His entire wealth consisted of a black hair-covered water bag which smelled strongly of tar, a leather apron to protect his clothes, and a brass goblet that shone like gold to which a bell was attached by a metal chain. El-Arbi was barefoot and his head was covered by a threadbare turban ornamented with kauris to ward off the evil eye. The cloak he wore had been white when he had first received it as a gift on the day of Aid el-Kbir, a long time ago. He trudged from morning until nightfall through the narrow streets of the *medina* to the

wells of brackish water which were to be found midway
between the town and the dunes. He would ring his bell to
draw the attention of the passers-by.

"Water! Who would like some water!" was his cry.

"Give me a cupful of water, for Allah has blessed you,"
was the reply of a customer as he placed the seventh part
of a sou in the water-carrier's hand. El-Arbi would then
untie the leather strap that served to close the water pouch,
fill the brass goblet with water and hand it to the customer.

"May it solace your heart, may it appease your thirst!"

There were many, however, who did not possess even the
seventh part of a sou. They looked at the water pouch deject-
edly, then turned away with a shrug.

El-Arbi called to them, "By the voice of Allah! Drink, O
you who are thirsty!" He tendered them a full goblet, saying, "Take it in the name of Allah."

During the religious festivals when rich and poor alike
gave alms, El-Arbi filled his water pouch and, walking
among the crowds in the market place or on the road, he
distributed water without charge. Such an act of charity
was looked upon with favor by Allah, for at that time water
was scarce in Tangier, and happy was he who possessed a
well or cistern in the court of his home. El-Arbi even gave
water to animals, to plants that were drying out from the
heat, and even to the earth itself. At night he slept in a
dark cave which he shared with other water-carriers, who,
like himself, came from the southern part of Morocco. Lying
on his worn, discolored mat, he dreamed of his home, a land
of palm trees and dates. He wondered if he would ever
return there.

"Will I ever see the blond, sugary fruit of the palm tree
again, the murmuring streams, and the brown-skinned
women of my oasis?" he asked himself.

The water pouch became heavier with each passing day;
the inclined streets of the casbah seemed to grow steeper,

the sun was stronger; the rains seemed to him more frequent and colder than before. One day he began to use a cane and he began to carry water only to the sections of the town closest to the wells.

"I am growing old," he said to himself, but he was confident that Allah would not abandon him when he was no longer able to carry the water pouch.

Allah the Merciful sent him a peaceful death. Man dies only by the Will of Allah.

"The term of his life is ended," said his friends when they found the water-carrier stretched out lifeless on his mat one morning. They placed him on a litter; afterward they recited the holy suras and buried him.

On Judgment Day, El-Arbi awaited the two angels who judge the actions of the children of Adam. They arrived and began to interrogate him.

"You were one of those who believed in the Sublime Truths. Tell us of your deeds on earth," said the first angel.

"Your good deeds will be weighed against your evil deeds," said the second angel.

"Allah alone is perfect," said the water-carrier. "I have done evil and good like all living creatures, but it is said in Chapter X of the Koran that Allah will not ask more of a man than he is capable of giving. The Lord will not punish us for sins committed through oversight."

As he spoke there came the clear singing sound of a spring gushing out of the earth. Waves of pure clear water such as the water-carrier had distributed among his fellow creatures during his lifetime came pouring out of his tomb onto the grass of the countryside.

The Angels of Judgment lowered their flaming swords and their lips pronounced the following words:

"Blessed be the generous, for their reward is in the hands of Allah."

The Fig Tree

Among the precursors of Islam who wandered over the desert in search of Allah (the law of Islam had not yet been given to the Arab people) was an old man whose hair was completely white. He had marched for forty years over dense sand under the burning sun. The demons who were hidden between the rocks had called to him in lugubrious tones; jinn had frightened him by their hideous aspects in order to drive him back into the path of idolatry and sin. But the old man would not be deterred from his search, for his heart yearned to know Allah the Exalted. The years bore down on him; fatigue overwhelmed him; he was tormented by doubts, and despair took hold of his soul.

"I shall never find Allah," he said to himself one evening. He lay down on the ground and hoped death would overtake him. The world was still; the jinn had ceased their clamor and the demons had grown silent. The old man raised his eyes toward the sky and saw that there was rejoicing in the heavens. Overhead were myriads of stars, the flaming torches that the angels threw at the children of Ibliss (Allah curse the Evil One) who had been led by curiosity to spy on the celestial festivities. The old man fell asleep and dreamed that an angel came to see him.

"Rejoice, O Hanif [Believer]," said the angel, "a child is

born this night in Mecca, in the land of Arabia. He brings to men the truth that you have been seeking for so long."

"Alas," said the old man, "the child has just been born and I am at death's door. I shall not learn the path of salvation from his lips. I have wandered in search of a revelation from Allah. Alas, I have done nothing that might benefit mankind. I have existed on this earth like a cloud without rain, like a well filled with sand. I am less than the tree or the spring. Would that my span of life were extended so that I might live to see the Envoy of Allah."

"The hour of destiny has arrived," said the angel, "nothing can change that. Your wish, however, will be accorded, for he who searched for the light will not know the shadows of the tomb without having seen the birth of the morning. You will continue to live, but you will live as a tree. You will push your roots into the earth, not far from a spring and you will grow and prosper. You will nourish mankind and one day you will shelter the Prophet of Allah under your leaves."

The old Hanif became a fig tree whose leaves cast a deep shadow and whose fruits were like little bottles filled with honey. And so to this day fig trees stand at the edge of springs and in orchards. The birds of the sky gather on the branches of the fig tree; men and their flocks seek out the coolness of its shade; the Kabyles and those who inhabit the dry countries where rocks abound subsist on its fruit. He who plants a fig tree is a benefactor of mankind; on Judgment Day he will be pardoned of as many sins as a fig contains seeds.

Zeineb

Before Moulay Idriss (Allah protect him) had founded the city of Fez, Holy Islam was still unknown to the sun-worshiping inhabitants of Morocco. One of these inhabitants, a poor peasant named Hamou, had built his hut on the summit of a mountain. There he lived with his beautiful wife, Zeineb, whose complexion was as white as a pearl in its shell.

Like all the men of his race and his tribe, Hamou cultivated the land, led his sheep to pasture, went hunting, and joined in raids on other tribes. Zeineb prepared his meals, wove his garments, and helped in the fields at harvest time.

One day when she was in the fields with her scythe, Zeineb accidentally stepped on a snake. The snake bit her heel and Zeineb cried out in pain. She grew pale and began to tremble—a few hours later she died in the arms of her husband. At the death of Zeineb, the light seemed to go out of the eyes of the peasant Hamou; he neglected his fields and left his sheep to die. He remained day and night at the tomb of his beloved, calling to her in the most tender terms he knew and reproaching her gently for having abandoned him.

"O Zeineb, my beloved wife," he said, "with you have disappeared my joys and my hopes."

Tears burned his eyelids, fasting and sleepless nights

consumed his flesh. His reason gradually began to leave him like the flame of the lamp which dies out slowly for lack of oil.

Now it came to pass that the Prophet Jesus Christ (prayer and salvation be upon him) was journeying through the land of Morocco, when he came upon the hut of the peasant Hamou. He heard the lamentations of the poor man and was touched by his sorrow. Lifting his hands to the sky, he prayed, then commanded in a loud voice:

"Rise up, Zeineb!"

The tomb opened at his call and Zeineb appeared looking as young and beautiful as on the day of her wedding. She was dazzled by the daylight, for she had grown accustomed to the darkness of the subterranean regions. After a few moments she opened her eyes and stretched like someone coming out of a long sleep. She noticed Hamou, who was staring at her with unbelieving eyes.

"Who are you?" she asked, "and why do you gaze at me so?"

"I am your husband, Hamou, O Zeineb. Don't you recognize me?"

"You, my husband?" she said, laughing. "A beggar in rags with hollow cheeks and dull eyes?"

"O gazelle, I have mourned you for a very long time. Tears have burned my cheeks, misery and fasting have eaten my flesh."

"Why should that matter to me, O Hamou? I did not ask you to mourn me. I do not love you, for you are old and ugly—leave me in peace."

Then Zeineb smiled flirtatiously at Lord Jesus and turned on her heel. She began to descend down the mountain path with a graceful, nimble step.

The Son of Miriam (peace be upon her), indignant at

126

Zeineb's ingratitude, stamped on the ground and commanded:

"Open, O Earth!"

The bowels of the earth opened up and Zeineb, the ingrate, disappeared forever into a chasm of fire and smoke.

To this very day, travelers approaching the city of Moulay Idriss can see a light vapor from afar being wafted to and fro by the wind. It is the smoke rising from the chasm opened by the malediction of Jesus Christ.

Why Man Must Struggle to Obtain His Daily Bread

After Adam was driven out of blessed Paradise, he would stretch out his hand toward the tree branches, but he found none of the delicious fruits which had nourished him up to that time.

"Must I die then?" he asked himself and wept.

Allah, who is great and merciful, may His name be exalted, heard the voice of Adam and sent the angel Gabriel to succor him.

"Do not weep," said the angel to Adam. "I will teach you to draw food from the earth, for this earth is to be henceforth your habitation and domain. The food will sustain you and Eve and those born of your union."

The angel Gabriel held in his left hand some smooth brown grains, while his right hand held tight a leafless branch of a carob tree. With the aid of the branch he cut a perfectly straight furrow in the earth. He tossed in the seeds which he held in his left hand and blessed them. Leaves rose from the ground; they were small and green in color and the stems stood erect. The ears were swollen with wheat kernels.

"The benediction of Allah," said the angel. He praised the Lord, then cut the ears of wheat and rubbed the kernels between his palms. He blew on them to remove the chaff and then crushed the grains between two round stones.

"Are we supposed to be content with crushed grains of wheat?" asked Eve skeptically.

Gabriel poured pure water on the white powder which had come from the crushed wheat; he made a paste of it and then molded it into the shape of a full moon.

"Go, Adam, and gather some wood in the forest," said Gabriel.

Adam gathered together some branches which had fallen from the trees and had been dried by the sun; he placed them before the celestial visitor.

"Blow on the wood!" commanded Gabriel.

Adam blew and the first flame spurted high, clear and brilliant.

"This is another blessing of the Lord," said Adam. "Allah gave us this light in order to make the nights clear."

Gabriel put the dough which he had molded in the shape of a moon near the fire. The dough took on a light brown color—an agreeable odor issued from it.

"Put it in your mouth," said the angel Gabriel.

The bread slipped out of Adam's hand and he was compelled to run after it. Eve also took up the chase until she was out of breath.

"Must we always run after the bread before we can eat it?" said Eve to Gabriel.

128

The angel Gabriel answered her, "Yes, you will have to pursue the bread because you have doubted the words of the Lord."

Since that time man runs and tires himself out in the pursuit of bread.

The Almond Tree

Jasmina was about to be married. The women of her village bedecked her in sumptuous wedding attire; her sisters made her a crown of jasmine and pearls. The man who was to be her husband, a rich caid of the Atlas Mountains, waited for her in his castle.

Her friends said to Jasmina, "You are beautiful, and good fortune will be yours. Be of good cheer."

But there was no joy in her heart. The young bride wept bitterly, for the one who was destined to be her husband was not the man she loved. Since childhood she had loved her cousin Abderrahman, the handsomest and most valiant warrior of his tribe.

"Why does he not come to save me?" Jasmina asked herself. "Why are his friends indifferent while his happiness and mine is being destroyed?"

But Jasmina was wrong; Si Abderrahman and his friends were hidden behind the hedges waiting for the *ammaria* ("wedding palanquin") to pass. The servants of the caid followed on the heels of the palanquin with sword and spear

129

in hand, for in those violent times no one was sure of his life.

At a turn in the road which led from the bride's village to the caid's mountain castle, some armed men suddenly leaped from hiding and attacked the cortege.

"Give us the bride!" they cried. "Give us the bride!"

The servants and friends of the caid grouped themselves around the *ammaria* and defended it against Abderrahman and his men. A fierce battle ensued. Abderrahman and his group were the victors, but at the very moment that Abderrahman was leading the bride out of the palanquin a mountaineer struck him down with his lance.

Jasmina watched him grow pale and finally collapse; his blood reddened the ground beneath him. She threw herself upon his body and wept aloud.

"I shall rejoin you in the earth. I will be your wife in death since I cannot be yours in life."

Jasmina remained with him as long as he was alive. Then she covered him with her veil and left his body in the care of his friends and went away. The servants of the caid searched for the young woman in the village and throughout the countryside, but to no avail—they did not find her that day, nor any other day.

On the tomb of Abderrahman the warrior was seen to grow a tree of a hitherto unknown species. It was Jasmina, transformed into an almond tree by Allah, who had been moved by her fidelity. Every year on the anniversary of Si Abderrahman's death, the tree bedecks herself with leaves and strews the tomb of her beloved with perfumed, rose-tinted flower petals.

Fekroune the Tortoise

Many years ago there was a woman living in a Riff village who was skillful in the art of cutting and assembling cloth. She cut cloth without a fault; she sewed a *djellaba* with as many tiny stitches as there were grains of rice in a *tajin* (Moroccan dish).

Unfortunately, the woman was dishonest. To provide clothing for her children she would always ask for one or two lengths of cloth above the amount which was necessary for making a garment. As long as she robbed only the rich caids of the region, Allah was merciful and gave her time to repent. One day, however, she cheated a poor peasant; she made him a *djellaba* that was too short for him, with sleeves that were too tight and a hood that was far too narrow. It was winter; snow fell on the mountains and ice formed on the plains. The peasant's legs were bare under his too-short tunic; the wind hurt his eyes for the hood was too narrow. The cold penetrated his bones; it reached his heart and he died.

Allah cursed the seamstress; she was compelled henceforth to carry on her back tiny squares of cloth to remind her of the cloth she had robbed from her clients. He enclosed her, except for her head, her tail (Allah added this appendage), and her feet, in a narrow, hard prison that she drags about with her wherever she goes. For she was

131

transformed into Fekroune the Tortoise, whose malevolent
eyes resemble those of a snake and whose flesh trembles
even after death because of the Divine Curse.

For Allah is most learned in the way of the Truth!

The Chameleon

There was a time, many years ago, when Sidna Mohammed (prayer and salvation be upon him) was compelled
to flee from his enemies. He crossed one country and another
and finally came to the Atlas Mountains. His enemies were
closing in on him—he didn't know where to hide. All
about him were massive rocks; he noticed a cleft in the
largest of the rocks and decided to hide himself in it. His
enemies could not find him, since the cork oak and the
dwarf palms hid the cleft from view and the turtle doves
suspended their nests so as to conceal the Envoy of Allah.
Unfortunately, a Berber peasant woman had seen the
Prophet hide himself.

When the enemies of our Lord approached, they only
saw huge rocks hidden by the straight branches of the cork
oak and the wide leaves of the dwarf palms. Turtle doves
were flying about their nests repeating their refrain, "Praise
Allah!" "Praise Allah!"

"Let us go," said the leader of the group. "Mohammed
the Koreishite couldn't have hidden here, for the branches
of the cork oaks would have been broken where he had

passed through and the timid turtle doves would have flown away."

The Berber peasant woman, who was cutting wood nearby, overheard their conversation.

"Only a fool can be deceived by trees and birds," she sang mockingly.

"Woman, if you were here a few minutes ago," said the leader, "you must have seen a pale young man with black hair pass by. Isn't he hidden between the rocks or under some branches? Show us his shelter if you know where it is."

"What will you give me if I point it out to you?" she asked.

"We will give you a purse full of gold!"

The woman turned her eyes in the direction of the rock entrance in which Sidna Mohammed was hiding. But it was not in Allah's plans to allow His Envoy to perish thus; for He who abhors evil and punishes treason transformed the peasant woman into a hideous little reptile. A curse follows her wherever she goes. In vain does she hide in the clefts of rocks, in vain does she take on the color of her surroundings; sorcerers and magicians seek her out and kill her for their rituals.

Abdullah the Highwayman

There was once a brigand named Abdullah who lived deep in a forest on the Atlas Mountains. In his childhood and early youth he knew all the misery and humiliation that is the lot of the poor. He rebelled against the injustice he had suffered; someday he would be avenged.

"I will kill a hundred children of Adam," he said to himself one day, "to pay for the death of my father, who died in prison, and for the shame of my sisters, who have become prostitutes."

He bought a dagger and a gun and hid himself in a cave in the heart of the *manora* ("forest"). At night he would attack any travelers who might happen to come through the forest. His mother had followed him to his mountain retreat, for he was all she had left in the world; but she lived in fear and repentance, for she was old and saw the approach of death. She had a humble and submissive heart; she could not understand her son's revolt against fate.

One winter night a terrible storm struck the forest; rain fell in icy torrents, rivers overflowed their banks, and their waters inundated the fields and roads. A poor pilgrim coming from Hejaz was making his way through the forest. He had been walking since early morning and was looking for a place where he could stop and rest for the night; he was a man of many years and his body was "a weight to his soul."

134

"Allah has sent me shelter," he said to himself, for he could distinguish a fire burning deep in the forest and he rejoiced at the thought of the warmth. He was a stranger in this part of the country and did not know that a robber had set up his hiding place there between the trees and the rocks. The pilgrim pushed his way through the thick foliage to the hiding place, a cave, and demanded the hospitality of Allah.

The mother of Abdullah said to the stranger, "O my brother, leave this place if your life means anything to you. My son, who is master here, is a highway robber. He has sworn to kill a hundred children of Adam to avenge the wrongs which we have suffered. He has already put to death ninety-nine unfortunates—are you not afraid of being the hundredth?"

"My sister," answered the pilgrim, "the night is so terrible that even the animals, who are free of sin, shudder before the wrath of the Heavens."

"True, the night is terrible, but the fire of the sky and the hurricane winds are not fiercer than my son."

"The cold and the wind will kill me as surely as your son's dagger, O my sister. Let me rest at your hearth and taste the bread of hospitality. Whatever shall befall me is the Will of Allah."

The old woman then made room for the pilgrim before the *mejmar* ("clay stove"). She gave him a bowl of soup, some bread and meat, and a glass of tea. After the old man had eaten his portion, she pointed to a mat which lay in a dark corner of the cave.

"Sleep, O my brother," said the old woman. "If my son does not notice you I will say nothing and tomorrow after his departure I will show you the way out of the forest. If by unhappy chance my son should see you, I will beg him in the name of Allah the Almighty to spare your life."

"May the Lord bless you and reward you," said the old

man. Then, after having sat by the fire a while to dry out his clothes, he stretched out on the mat in the far corner of the cave and went to sleep.

The mother of Abdullah sat down before the fire; she turned her spindle and sang an old air from her youth to distract her from the thoughts that tormented her—for a song lulls to sleep one's sorrows.

> Spin a fine thread for Sidi Amar,
> Fine and brilliant for my lord.
> I will weave elegant cloth for Sidi Amar, my lord.
> The tailor will make a burnous with many folds.
> Embroidered with silk for Sidi Amar, my lord.
> The sun will bleach it,
> The wind that passes will gently waft
> The white burnous of my lord.

The spindle creaked as it turned; the flame of the *qandil* ("oil lamp") flickered; the old woman nodded her head in sleep.

The brigand came home very late that night, for he had been delayed by the storm. He was in a terribly angry mood; he looked like a wolf who was returning to his den after a fruitless hunt.

"Give me something to eat, mother," he said, "and throw some wood on the stove so that I may dry out my clothes."

The mother obeyed without a word.

The highwayman ate lustily. He drank hot tea and warmed his hands at the stove. After he had eaten his fill, he decided to go to bed. Suddenly he noticed the pilgrim's staff.

"Who has been here?" he asked.

"Who would enter the cave of a lion, O my son? Who would not fear to come here even in your absence?"

"The children of Adam have pursued the wolf right into his den. You are trembling, mother. Tell me, is someone here?"

136

The old woman came over to Abdullah; she placed her trembling hands on his heart.

"You have just come from the forest," she said. "You have seen the horror of this winter night. You know what misery and suffering mean. A pilgrim, an old man bent with age, knocked at our door and asked for hospitality. He was soaked to the skin. Should I have sent him back out into the cold and the rain?"

"No, you couldn't do that, mother."

Abdullah stretched out on his mat, but he couldn't sleep. Though the feeling of pity was alien to him, he somehow felt sorry for the aged pilgrim, a man whose many years were reflected in his snow-white hair; the old man had used his last ounce of strength to make the holiest of pilgrimages. Abdullah wept as he thought of all the evil he had done in his life. When the dawn came, he arose from his mat. Then he filled a jug with water and woke up the pilgrim.

"Father, it is the hour of prayer," he said. "Here is the water for your ablutions."

After the old man had made his prayers, Abdullah filled his sack with the choicest things in his cave—bread, dates, and cheese. He slipped two pieces of silver into the old man's hand.

"Take them," he said, "they will serve you for the rest of your journey."

Abdullah accompanied the old man to the edge of the forest. There he bade him farewell, first kissing him on the forehead and then on the shoulder.

"Go with the protection of Allah."

"May salvation be upon you," the pilgrim replied. "Allah the Merciful is the Sovereign of the Universe."

At the foot of a steep mountain whose summit was eternally wrapped in a turban of snow, there once lived a holy saint. He belonged to a religious sect whose members wore garments of white wool. His life was devoted to prayer and fasting. Before renouncing the world in order to live in the contemplation of Allah, this saint had been a powerful lord. He had never known the terrible privations of poverty and the contempt and humiliation which the poor must undergo at the hands of the rich. His life consisted of doing good deeds and meditating the Divine Word. The end of his existence was close at hand, but he awaited it with calm resignation.

One morning as the saintly man turned toward the Qibla ("direction of Mecca"), the Angel of the Lord entered his house and placed two breads on a stone—a white bread baked of fine wheat and perfumed with anise and fennel and a black bread hardened with bran. He also put down two clusters of grapes. One cluster consisted of heavy, gold-colored grapes and the other was a small, silver-colored cluster. Then the angel departed.

"Why did the Angel of the Lord bring me two breads and two clusters of grapes today?" the saint asked himself. When he had finished his prayer, an old man, vanquished by age and suffering, came to his door.

"I am your guest in the name of Allah," said the stranger after many salutations.

"Welcome!" said the scholar coolly. He asked the pilgrim to enter his hut made of tree limbs. Then he broke the black bread into two pieces; he tore the cluster of silver-gilt grapes in two and offered the smaller halves of each to the stranger.

"This is all that I possess," he lied.

He said to himself, "For twenty years I have never missed my prayers to Allah. I have renounced the goods of this world in order to attain perfection and live close to the Lord. However, I have never received from Heaven more than a loaf of black bread and a cluster of inferior grapes.

138

Does this pilgrim, who has been to Mecca like so many others, deserve to have the white bread and the muscat grapes that the Angel of the Lord had brought for me?" In carrying thoughts of this nature, the saintly man could be likened to a rock covered with dust: a strong shower of rain washes the dust away and the hardness of the rock is revealed underneath.

That evening, when deep shadows had completely obliterated the horizon, the awesome Angel of Death came to take the souls of the pilgrim, the scholar, and the highway robber so as to conduct them before Allah, may His name be exalted.

"My son," said the Lord to the pilgrim, "you were poor, old, and yet you had confidence in my protection. Despite a thousand dangers, you have made the holiest of pilgrimages. You may live in Paradise and eat of the fruits of happiness which grow there. Whatever your heart desires will be yours."

The pilgrim rejoiced at the reward which Allah had accorded him. His head was encircled by a radiant light like a halo. Then our Lord called for Abdullah, whose face was veiled with the shadow of gloom. It was turned toward the dark regions where the souls of those who had done evil in their lifetimes repeated in mournful tones, "If we had only known, if we had only known."

"You have been persecuted all your life," said the Almighty to the highwayman. "You were unjustly treated at the hands of your fellow men. This is what has made you wicked and cruel, for the proud heart revolts against injustice. But pity finally moved your heart of stone. You have shown love and reverence for this aged pilgrim and you have wept the tears of repentance. You may remain in Paradise."

The saintly scholar thought to himself, "Since these two men have been received into Paradise, the one for having made a pilgrimage to Mecca and the other for merely repenting a life of crime, there can be no question in my case, whose life has been devoted to continuous prayer and adoration of the Lord."

Allah, who can see into men's hearts, looked at him severely.

"I am not unjust to those who serve me," He said. "You have never known misfortune or suffered the contempt of your fellow men—it is even harder to bear than pain. You are well learned in the ways of religion and yet you did not hesitate to pretend to the pilgrim that you had no other bread than black bread and no other grapes than those of inferior quality. Your place is with the demons in Hell."

For the justice of Allah has no parallel.

The Dream of the Sage's Wife

The beasts in the forest, the birds who fly through the air, are as much His creatures as we are, for they too will appear before the Almighty. So it is inscribed in the Holy Book.
—The Koran, Chapter VI, verse 18

Zoubeida was an elderly lady of Marrakech, the wife of a sage. She was known far and wide for her learning and her generosity. She read the Book of Books, sought the wisdom of Allah, and distributed generous alms to the poor.

One night she lay awake meditating the Divine Word and questioning in her mind the true principles of perfection. When sleep finally overtook her she had a curious dream. She found herself on a wide road of blood-red earth. She walked and walked until she came to a garden. Here there were gushing fountains, tall trees, and brilliantly colored flowers exuding a sweet strong perfume.

"Never have I seen such beautiful flowers in the courtyard of Fez or in the orange groves of Tetuan," thought the wife of the sage. "They must certainly come from India or China."

She approached close to the flowers and noticed that some were as fresh as the morning dew and others were pale and drooped toward the ground.

"What garden is this?" she asked herself. "And to what sultan does it belong?"

A young man came toward her. He had a gentle appearance, with skin as white as a pearl. Although the lady had not spoken aloud, he divined her question.

"This garden is the blessed Paradise," he said. "It is written in the Book of Books, 'When the sky opens, it will be as brilliant as the rose.' "

"Tell me, what is the name of this tree which stands in the middle of the garden?" asked Zoubeida.

"It is Nabec, whose branches have no thorns," was the answer.

"And what are these flowers called?"

"These flowers are the souls of those who will be guided by the Lord."

"Are any of these flowers the souls of people I knew?"

"Yes," said the young man. "This flower whose center is gold and purple is the soul of Yacouta, your servant; that flower whose blue corolla is striped with black like the wings of a butterfly is Rihana, the wife of Si Hamou the cobbler."

"And this flower which is the most beautiful of all? Is it the soul of a saint or a sultan?"

"That flower which blooms eternally is the soul of Baba Driss, the begger in your neighborhood."

"Do the souls of the living dwell in Paradise before their death?" asked Zoubeida in astonishment. "Rihana, my neighbor, is dead, but Yacouta, my servant, and Baba Driss are still alive; at least they were alive when I retired to my room for meditation."

"They are still among the living."

"Tell me, may the Lord bless you, can I find my soul here—assuming that it is worthy to be in the Lord's Paradise?"

A flower was pointed out to her which resembled the hyacinth but whose tarnished glow was reminiscent of the crescent moon when a fine mist veils the nocturnal sky.

"How pale my soul is," said the sage's wife with great disappointment. "Am I less worthy than Rihana, the cobbler's widow, or Yacouta, my servant?"

"Rihana visited prisoners and tended the sick without fear of contagion," said the young man. "Yacouta never forgets to place two buckets of water before the door, so that man and beast may quench their thirst."

"But how is it that Baba Driss the beggar is the most favored of all?" asked Zoubeida in anger, for she considered herself a model of piety and wisdom. "Has he studied the Koran as I have done? Does he seek wisdom like a greedy man looking for gold? Has he made the holy pilgrimage to Mecca? What has he done to merit such honor? What claim does he have to perfection?"

"Perfection lies in sincere love of Allah and compassion for all living creatures. Driss loves the Almighty with all the simplicity of his heart. For love of Him, he succors the humblest of His creatures. Since he is too poor to come to the aid of his fellow man, he looks after the mute creatures: the hungry cat, the stray dog, and the wounded bird find a friend in him. He treats his donkey with gentleness.

He waters the parched plant standing in sun-baked earth."

"Is there greater virtue in giving our bread to dogs than to children who are in want?" asked Zoubeida with irony.

"Generosity of the heart lies in alleviating the misery of all living creatures, for all are on this earth by the grace of Allah. The Prophet of Allah, prayer and salvation be upon him, urges that you be gentle toward all living creatures. Remember how he took a gazelle under his protection after she had been pursued by hunters, how he cut away part of his garment so as not to disturb a cat and her kittens who had been lying on it."

"Are my prayers and the charity I have given worth nothing?"

"Everything has its value. To caress a dog hungry for tenderness, to give your donkey a handful of fresh grass during its period of rest, or to provide seed for birds during the winter season has as much merit in the eyes of Allah as giving charity or reciting the holiest of prayers. Now as for you, you drove your dog out of the house one cold winter night, you struck a cat who stole a mite of your food, and you have kept a bird prisoner who had entered your house to ask for hospitality."

The wife of the sage understood and was humbled.

"I have sinned," she said, "and I repent. If Allah in His mercy will accord me a few more years of life, I will love and cherish all His creatures, from the noblest to the lowliest."

As she spoke, the beautiful garden disappeared before her eyes. She knew that a dream had been sent to her by the Lord in order to guide her in the path of salvation. She remembered the words of the angel, "The principle of perfection is in the love of Allah and pity for His creatures." The sage's wife became as kind and generous toward Allah's mute creatures as she was toward human beings.

Why the Mohammedan Does Not Eat Pork

Years ago, when the Prophet of Allah (prayer and salvation be upon him) walked upon the earth, there lived in a village of Syria a skillful hunter named Omar ben Rachid. He hunted the gazelle and even the lion held no terror for him, for his arrow always found its mark.

One winter day he killed some wild boars. He distributed the meat to the members of his village, giving the best parts of each animal to the poor and keeping the rest for his friends and his family. Unfortunately, he forgot to give a share of meat to a certain poor widow who was blessed with many children.

That night, while the people of the village were feasting on boar meat, the unfortunate widow and her children were suffering the pangs of hunger. The widow wept bitterly. Finally she carried her plea to the Lord.

"Omar the hunter has forgotten us. I am hungry and my children are starving before my very eyes."

The Lord listened carefully to her words, for His ear is never deaf to the pleas of the unfortunate. He had pity on her. To avenge her, He sent pestilence and death and finally a terrible hurricane to the village, the likes of which the inhabitants of Syria had never known. The frightened villagers brought gifts to Sidna Omar el-Hattab, the cadi of the Prophet, whose wisdom and justice were known to all.

144

"Why does the Lord torment us so mercilessly?" they asked.

"Try to remember if you committed a grave sin," said the cadi. "Did you drive away the wanderer who came before your tent and begged your hospitality in the name of Allah? Did you turn from the beggar, the afflicted, the orphan, or the widow?"

"Alas, in sharing the meat from Omar's hunt we forgot the widow and her children," the villagers suddenly remembered.

"The widow's plea was heard by Allah, for He has punished you," said the cadi. "You will henceforth never touch that part of the boar which is reserved for the widow."

The villagers repented and promised to do as the cadi commanded. But they did not remember which part of the boar was usually set aside for the widow and her children. Not wishing to incur divine anger, they ceased eating pork altogether.

How Sidna Youssef Invented the Clock

Zuleika, wife of the king of Egypt, was seized with a great passion for a young man named Youssef.

"Allah is my refuge," said Youssef, "I will not sin. I have been showered with gifts in this palace. Shall I deceive my master? Evil befalls an ingrate."

He tried to flee, but Zuleika followed him and tore his

cloak. To further her vengeance she called down the wrath of the king upon Youssef.

"Youssef broke into my apartment and I have torn his cloak defending my honor. What punishment does he deserve, O King?" said the Queen.

One of the king's relatives said, "If the coat is torn in front, Zuleika tells the truth. If it was torn in the back, it is she who is guilty and Youssef who is innocent."

The coat was found to be torn in the back.

"Let us keep this knowledge to ourselves," said the king.

But who could keep the tongues of the slave-girls from wagging? Soon all the women of the town were laughing at the queen.

"Passion inflamed her heart," they said, and smiled.

The queen soon learned of this gossip and she took steps to justify her behavior. She prepared a grand feast to which she invited the wives of noblemen and wealthy citizens. While the ladies were dining and enjoying each other's company, Zuleika brought Youssef before them. The women were so charmed by the young man's handsome appearance that many forgot they held dinner knives in their hands and cut their fingers accidentally.

"But this man is more than a slave," they said. "He is an angel."

"It is he who has made me guilty in your eyes," said the queen. "If he will not requite my passion, I will have him locked away in a dark prison."

"I prefer prison to committing a sin," said Youssef.

Again Zuleika invented some new lies in order to turn the king against Youssef. The king called together a council. He invited the viziers, wise men, and priests of his realm.

"What punishment do you suggest for a man who has given offense to the throne?" asked the king.

"What is the religion of the guilty man?"

"He follows the law of Abraham, Isaac, and Jacob. He does not worship our idols."

"Put him in an underground cell," advised the council. "He won't know how to tell the hours of prayer and he won't know when to kneel before his God."

The viziers and wise men mocked Youssef, for they were idol-worshipers and the son of Jacob worshiped the Master of the Universe.

"Where is your God?" they chided. "Call to Him so that He may save you."

They rejoiced at his plight as they put him in the hands of soldiers. He was thrown into a cell deep in the earth with other prisoners who had incurred the wrath of the king.

"O my companions of misfortune," said Youssef to his fellow inmates, "why should we worship heathen idols instead of the one God who is omnipotent, whose power extends throughout the Universe?"

The other prisoners listened to him; they were convinced that he spoke the truth and one by one they were converted to the religion of salvation. Their hearts rejoiced with the new religion but their spirits were saddened, for they could not tell the hours of prayer in the darkness of the underground cell,

"Pray to Allah, He will hear your voice," the prisoners urged Youssef.

Youssef lauded Allah the Almighty and prayed to Him. The Lord, praised be His name, sent Sidna Djabril (prayer and salvation be upon him) down to earth to show Youssef how to build an instrument capable of replacing the sun, moon, and stars in telling time. Youssef, following his counsel, took up the large clay pot in which the prisoners received their daily rations. He then placed a metal goblet in the center of the vessel. Then he cut some rushes out of his

147

mattress, procured some palm fibers, and with these materials made the dial plate, wheelworks, and hands of a clock. It was now possible for the prisoners to respect the hours of prayer to Allah despite the darkness of their cell.

Thus it was that Sidna Youssef made the first clock. It later served as a model to the men of Massai, of Younan, and even to the Christians.

The Dogs of Tangier

Why do the dogs of Tangier bark louder than all other dogs on this earth?

When Houteifa the swallow brought back to Noah (peace be upon him) a bit of the black earth which she had taken from the Oued Charf, the prophet, aware that the skies had closed and that the earth would soon absorb the waters, directed the Ark toward the highest summit of the Atlas Mountains. There the Ark came to rest.

"Praise to Allah!" said Noah, "for He has shown His mercy and has saved us from the fury of the waters."

Noah opened the door of the Ark and descended toward the plain with his children and his flocks. In each of the Moroccan towns he offered a sacrifice to Allah as a sign of gratitude. Unfortunately, when he came to Tangier, neither heifers nor rams remained to be sacrificed, only the dogs who had guarded his flocks.

148

"I must give what I possess," Noah said to himself. "Since I still have my dogs I shall sacrifice them."

Why did he not sacrifice the tigers or the lions he had brought with him in the Ark? Alas, the powerful are always spared and it is the weak who are sacrificed in their stead. The dogs recounted to Noah all the services they had rendered him; they had defended him against Seid the lion and Noumir the panther; by their vigilance they had saved his youngest son from Doubba the crafty hyena. But the dogs pleaded in vain—Noah sacrificed his faithful servitors.

Indignant at such ingratitude and injustice, the dogs of Tangier still bark in protest against the murder of their brothers. All in vain, alas. What ear, other than that of Allah, heeds the cry of the unfortunate and the weak?

The Crow

In the beginning of time, the crow was as white as the dove but his heart was as black as night. It was he who witnessed the death of Abel at the hands of his brother Cain. The crow called to Cain and advised him how to hide his crime.

"Bury him in the earth," he said, "and shield him from the eyes of Allah."

As if anything could be hidden from the Lord.

149

Allah's indignation was so great that He punished the bird; He compelled him to perch on a limb underneath which burned a fire of green wood. The smoke darkened the plumage of the bird and he became as black as coal, as black as his crime.

Since that time, his presence is always a presage of evil and his cry freezes the hearts of men. For where he passes, friends part and even lovers forget each other.

Glossary

agouza: "old crone"

Aid el-Kbir: festival of the sheep sacrifice.

Allah: the Supreme Being of Islam.

ammaria: "wedding palanquin"

Azrael: the angel who separates the soul from the body at the moment of death. The Angel of Death.

babour: "guide"

bahria: "inhabitant of the sea"

baqualat: "storekeepers"

bedaiah: "vest"

beignets: flat cakes or fritters.

burnous: a hooded mantle or cloak, open down the front.

cab-cabs: wooden sandals.

cadi: an inferior magistrate or judge, usually the judge of a town or village.

caftan: robe of honor

caid: the head of a tribe; the chief of a district or group of villages.

caliph: a title of the successor of Mohammed, both as temporal and spiritual ruler. The first four caliphs were Abu Bekr, Omar, Othman, and Ali.

casbah: Arabic word for "fort," but has come to mean the native quarter (i.e. the section in which Moslems were confined in Arabic cities dominated by Europeans).

charqui: a light, but steady breeze.

cherbils: "slippers"

couscous: a dish prepared of groats mixed with salt water, sometimes with vegetables or meat added.

151

Dehour: "midday prayer"

dervish: a member of any various Moslem fraternities or orders taking vows of poverty and austerity. The members either live together in monastic societies or wander from place to place as friars. Also known as fakirs.

djellaba: a full-length hooded cloak or robe, slipped on over the head.

Djenna: "Paradise" (Garden of Eden).

faquih: a scholar and teacher of the Koran.

farran: "baker"

fouta: a gown.

hauma: the native quarter of a town or city (*see* casbah).

Hanif: a Believer; an orthodox Moslem; specifically, any of a number of men in Arabia before, or of, Mohammed's time who maintained vague monotheistic ideas and sought a better religion, probably influenced by Judaism and Christianity. Mohammed was influenced by their doctrines.

hiai: "snake charmer"

hotba: a sermon; a speech; but also the request of a girl's hand in marriage.

Ibliss: Lucifer; the Devil; Satan.

Idriss, Moulay: patron saint of Fez.

Islam: the religion of the Moslems, with the creed, "There is no God but Allah, and Mohammed is His Prophet."

jinni: a nature demon (*plural,* jinn) of the wilderness or of savage and deserted places, representing the hostile and unsubdued forces of nature. They are either evil or good, depending on whether they follow the Mohammedan faith, and are supposed to be constituted of pure flame, with the ability to adopt different forms and become invisible. Often written as "genie," "genii," from the Latin for a spirit who presides over the destiny of a person or place.

jinniyeh: a female jinni.

Kabyles: a confederation of tribes in Algeria and Tunisia and a few oases in the Sahara; a branch of the Berber race. The Kabyles are Mohammedans, but propertly speaking, not Arabs.

They are known for their energy and enterprise, and even in modern times hold themselves apart from the Arabs in their common communities.

kasri: "shops"

kefta: brochettes of chopped meat.

kif: "hashish"

kisaria: the cluster of stalls in a *souk* which are devoted to the sale of textiles, clothing, and luxury articles.

Koran: the scriptures of the Mohammedans, containing the professed revelations to Mohammed. By Mohammed, the name "koran" was given to a single revelation or to a collection or revelations, but after his death, when his various utterances had been collected in writing, this name was applied to the whole book. The Koran is in Arabic, is divided in 114 suras, or chapters, and is the basis for the religious, social, civil, commercial, military, and legal regulation of the Mohammedan world.

Koreishite: a member of the Koreish, a powerful Arab tribe of which Mohammed was a member, which from early in the fifth century formed a kind of religious hierarchy having in charge the Kaaba at Mecca.

Lalla: "my lady" (milady); Madame.

Maghrib: "West Country." The term designates the western portion of Arab-populated North Africa—Morocco, Algeria, and Tunisia, as well as the western half of Libya—and according to some scholars, Spain, during and after the Moslem conquest. Also, that one of the five daily prayers which is observed at twilight.

manora: "forest"

marrah: "sheep enclosure"

Mecca: the birthplace of Mohammed and a holy city to the Moslems. The Kaaba—a small and nearly cubical stone building in the court of the Great Mosque—contains the Black Stone of Mecca, probably of meteoric origin, which is fabled to have been given by Gabriel to Abraham. The Kaaba represents the direction (Qibla) to which Moslems turn in praying. Since the time of Mohammed, the Kaaba has been the chief object of pilgrimage of the Islamic world.

medersa: Arabic university for study of the Koran.

medina: "city," or that part of a North African city built before the arrival of the Europeans.

Mehakma: Tribunal; court of law.

mejmar: "clay stove"

mektoub: "fate"

mellah: "ghetto"

mohandiz: "engineer"

Moulay: "my lord" (milord).

muezzin: the crier who, from a minaret or other part of a mosque, at stated hours five times daily, intones aloud the call summoning the Faithful to prayer.

negafa: "Negro servant"

oued: river"

oum: "mother"

pasha: an honorary title placed after the name; given to officers of high rank in Turkey, as for example, governors of provinces (Morocco was once a province).

Prophet, the: (always capitalized), Mohammed.

qalan: quill used for writing.

qandil: "oil lamp"

Qibla: the direction of Mecca; also written "kiblah." (*See* Mecca)

quaddid: meat cut in strips, salted, and left to dry in the sun.

Riff: the hilly coastal region of Morocco; also the name of the inhabitants of this region.

Sidi: "Sire"; "Sir"

Sidi Ali ben Hamdouch, Sidi Ali Bou-Ghaleb, Sidi Amar, Sidi Bouarraquia, Sidi Masmoudi, Sidi Mohammed ben Aissa, Sidi Qassem: patron saints of Morocco.

Sidna Djabril: the angel Gabriel.

souk: market place with open tents and stalls.

sultan: a title given to or assumed by any Mohammedan prince.

sura: one of the chapters or sections of the Koran.

tajin: a Moroccan plate or dish.

154

telmita: "divan cover"
tolba: a student at a *medersa*.

vizier: a principal helper of a Mohammedan sovereign.

Younan: Greece.

Zacoum: the infernal tree whose fruit was the heads of devils.